THE DARK SIDE OF HOPKINSVILLE

D1600728

THE DARK SIDE OF
HOPKINSVILLE
STORIES BY TED POSTON

Edited and Annotated by Kathleen A. Hauke

The University of Georgia Press   Athens and London

© 1991 by the University of Georgia Press
Published by the University of Georgia Press
Athens, Georgia 30602
All rights reserved

Designed by Erin Kirk
Set in Berkeley Old Style
by Tseng Information Systems, Inc.
Printed and bound by Thomson-Shore
The paper in this book meets the guidelines for permanence
and durability of the Committee on Production Guidelines for
Book Longevity of the Council on Library Resources.

Printed in the United States of America

95 94 93 92 91   5 4 3 2

Library of Congress Cataloging in Publication Data

Poston, Ted, 1906–1974.
The dark side of Hopkinsville / by Ted Poston :
edited and annotated by Kathleen A. Hauke.
p.   cm.
Includes bibliographical references (p.
ISBN 0-8203-1302-5 (alk. paper).
— ISBN 0-8203-1303-3 (pbk. : alk. paper)
1. Segregation—Kentucky—Hopkinsville—History—20th century.
2. Hopkinsville (Ky.)—Race relations.
3. Afro-Americans—Kentucky—Hopkinsville—History—20th century.
4. Poston, Ted, 1906–1974—Childhood and youth.
5. Afro-Americans—Kentucky—Hopkinsville—Biography.
6. Hopkinsville (Ky.)—Biography.
I. Hauke, Kathleen A.   II. Title.
F459.H8P67 1991
976.9'78—dc20   90-11251
                                                        CIP

British Library Cataloging in Publication Data available

The poem "Since Frazer Came to Hopkinsville"
was made available by Professor Luther P. Jackson.

Title page photo: Courtesy of William T. Turner

For Henry John LaFarge Hauke, Henry Lee Moon,
and Henry Allison Williams

CONTENTS

Acknowledgments   ix

List of Hopkinsville Informants   xiii

Introduction   xv

1. Mr. Jack Johnson and Me   1

2. The Werewolf of Woolworth's   9

3. Knee Baby Watkins   18

4. Cousin Blind Mary   31

5. Papa Was a Democrat   41

6. Mr. Beefer Jones   51

7. High on the Hog   60

8. The Birth of a Notion   72

9. Rat Joiner Whips the Kaiser   83

10. The Revolt of the Evil Fairies   92

Notes   97

Sources   105

ACKNOWLEDGMENTS

The search for Ted Poston began in 1980. Trudier Harris and Thadious Davis sent mimeographed letters to members of the College Language Association, stating that they were editing the Afro-American volumes of *The Dictionary of Literary Biography* and still needed critical essays on certain writers, including Ted Poston. I remembered a sprightly, vivid, action-packed article Poston had written on Langston Hughes for the *New York Post*. A gleaming, bespectacled black face had smiled out from the illustration of the article's author. I laughed. In those old days, his appearance and craft seemed incongruous; one rarely saw so black a reporter.

I wrote editors Harris and Davis, "May I write the essay on Ted Poston? I would like to find out more about him." First came the critical essay for the *DLB*. I discovered that I had missed Ted Poston in life by six years, but his widow, Ersa Hines Poston, was listed in *Who's Who*. She directed me to the executor of Poston's estate, Henry Lee Moon, his boon companion and fellow journalist, who carefully retrieved Poston's papers. Among them were these ten stories. They seemed a find. Mr. Moon said no, they had not all been published, and yes, he would permit me to seek a publisher.

A summer stipend from the National Endowment for the Humanities in 1984 enabled me to do research in New York City, the only location of microfilms holding the evidence of Poston's forty-two years in journalism. I spent many days in Harlem at the Schomburg Center for Research in Black Culture, part of the New York Public Library system, where, with Mr. C. Finney's help, I located and read the *Pittsburgh Courier* and the *New York Amster-*

dam News for the years Poston worked for them. Other days I spent at the New York Public Library Annex where the microfilms of the *New York Post* are stored in closed archives. Virginia Cheteyan, assistant to the editorial director of the *Post*, obtained permission for me to use the *Post* library after Poston's former colleague, Joe Kahn, told me to be sure to check the *Post*'s clipping and photo files.

When I first set off for Hopkinsville as a stranger, Ersa Poston advised, "Talk with Allison Williams!" Those words made all the difference. Williams, a lifelong chum of Ted Poston's, in whose home Poston lived as a teenager after the Poston family fell apart, invited me to use his home as a headquarters while doing my local research. Jo Anne Gabbard and Brooks Major of Hopkinsville Community College found an opening for me as teacher of one composition course and let the word out that I was available for talks in the community. This helped pay the rent. I thank Rev. A. R. Lasley of the Virginia Street Baptist Church for his encouragement and for entering a good word for this work at critical moments. I also thank Barbara Smith for her endorsement at the college.

But none of that would have helped without the people who talked. Ersa Poston had excitedly told me that at her husband's funeral she "met Rat Joiner!" hero of most of the stories. When Allison Williams graciously set up an interview for me with Joiner, my daughter Katy, an aficionado of the Hopkinsville stories, exulted, "You're going to meet Rat Joiner? Oh, he is such a treasure! He had such an exciting life and all by the age of nine!" Richard Hauke paid phone bills after I conducted long-distance interviews; bought reams of paper; listened to the moans and groans during moments of frustration; and as so many interviewees died of old age during the period of the work, reminded me how fortunate it was that I spoke with them while there was time.

Many other people and organizations helped me locate Ted Poston, including Ehrai Adams, Frederick Lee Atkins, Kathryn Atkins, Elnora Bivins, Dolores Brooks, Sarah Brooks, Mavis Bryant, Marshall Butler, Evelyn N. Cayce, Kenneth B. Clark, Jerry H. Conover, Georgianna Cumberbatch, Vivian Cunningham, Anita

Acknowledgments

Darnell, Bill Dillard, Dorothy F. Donnelly, Joel Dreyfuss, Margaret Dryden, James Duncan, Jr., James Duncan, Sr., Irving Eckman, Mollie Lee Moon Elliott, C. Gerald Fraser, Marjana Frising, Raymond Frye, Mary Gill, Harvard University Research Libraries, Nellie Hauke, Robert E. Hemenway, Ruth Hill, Alberta Holloway, Donald Holloway, Nathan I. Huggins, Russia Hughes, Jean Blackwell Hutson, Barbara Loomis Jackson, Esther Joiner Jackson, Marie Byrd Poston Jackson, Mayor of Hopkinsville Sherrill L. Jeffers, Sarah L. Jefferson, I. V. Joiner, Paul Joiner, James C. Killibrew, Rebecca Ladd, Allen Lake, Teresa LaPrade, Martha Ledford, Hylan Lewis, Mary Helen London, Cynthia Maude-Gembler, Ambrizella Maxwell, Bob Maynard, Nancy Hicks Maynard, Wanda McCombs, Manson Melton, Moorland-Spingarn Research Center of Howard University, Jessye Fraser Morgan, Lydia Braxton Moten, Larry Nathanson, Ray Nienaber, Bruce Ohr, Margaret Proctor, Betty and Mathew Quarles, Robert W. Roach, Betty Smith (Hopkinsville children's librarian), Marilyn Stokes, Tennessee State University's Special Collections, Frank J. Thomas, Bettye Thurmond, William J. Trent, Ann Trow, Alice Underwood, Theodore G. Vincent, Dorothy West, Francis Eugene Whitney, Bankie Williams, Clifford Wilson, Reginald Wilson, and Jan Zitniak.

Others are acknowledged in the source section of this book (pp. 105–6).

HOPKINSVILLE INFORMANTS

AW   Allison Williams

CWB   Charles W. Bronaugh

JKB   Jennie Knight Baker

JTL   J. T. Lynch

MDW   Mary Duncan Wilson

MQ   Marcus Quarles

TRJ   Theodore Roosevelt "Rat" Joiner

WTT   William T. Turner

INTRODUCTION

Ted Poston traveled far from his early twentieth-century childhood home in Hopkinsville, Kentucky, to become the first career-long black reporter for a major white metropolitan newspaper, a member of Franklin D. Roosevelt's "Negro Cabinet" in Washington in 1940 and, after thirty-five years at the *New York Post,* America's "Dean of Black Journalists." Poston proved the lesson instilled by his older brother, Robert Lincoln Poston: "You are just as good as *anyone.*" He helped change public opinion and law concerning the racial system by applying his verbal gifts to exposing racism's irrationality, and he illustrated black intelligence, creativity, and dignity. He worked as a reporter and city editor for the *New York Amsterdam News,* covered Harlem for the *Post,* and reported on black opinion and activity in the military for the U.S. Office of War Information during World War II. These jobs enabled him to make a wide audience aware of the conditions of black people from the 1930s through the 1960s. Poston's work brought him into contact with leading figures of the Harlem Renaissance, the Civil Rights Movement, and American culture in general.

Despite his sophisticated, cosmopolitan professional environment, however, Ted Poston's heart in reverie returned to Hopkinsville. With his livelihood established, Poston used leisure time for reminiscing on paper in ten short stories about "almost forgotten incidents from childhood" that he hoped to publish in a volume to be called *The Dark Side of Hopkinsville.* He felt that "someone should put down the not-always depressing experiences of a segregated society like the one I grew up in." Poston's entertaining, comical, historically revealing stories bear witness to the texture of a black child's life in a southern town at the beginning of the twentieth century. They show what a coterie of imaginative children did for fun, how their elders meddled, that the church was a facet of their common life, that families were close and extended, and that the Poston family felt driven, certain that mainstream society missed out by ignoring its darker brother.

Although Poston boasted of his own family's education, he considered knowledge gained on the streets to be as important as book-learning. He ridiculed pretension, especially among affluent, upwardly mobile "high yallers" who disdained people with darker skin. The departure of friends and other changes sadden Poston's young protagonists, but they remain undaunted, for they love life and inhabit a magical milieu in which they control their own destinies and often manipulate the adults' lives as well. Poston shows in the microcosm of childhood his view of how blacks in the macrocosm control and manipulate whites. No setback devastates. Poston's rollicking characters and problem-solvers meet every vicissitude creatively and with humor. Tough, very black little Rat Joiner licks white boys, outsmarts teachers, and even "whips the Kaiser" by devising a plan to win the World War I Liberty Bond Contest, which was so important that the white mayor visited the Booker T. Washington Colored Grammar School for the first time with an appeal to the children. Poston shows children learning to rely on their own wisdom as they act and gain confidence in themselves. They watch Bronco Billy and his Negro sidekick Pistol Pete at the movies, then go home and improvise—making Negro Pistol Pete the hero of their play and white Bronco Billy the one who bites the dust.

Detailed in the stories and in the memories of Poston's confreres are how to spend a day swimming, fishing, and cooking out without fishing poles, swimsuits, or picnic foods. In "Rat Joiner Whips the Kaiser," Poston reveals the patriotism of blacks even in the face of omnipresent racial discrimination. It was this paradox that so angered Robert Lincoln Poston. A truth emanating from "The

Revolt of the Evil Fairies" is that people must rebel against letting others see them as uninteresting, uncreative, and unworthy of respect or admiration. One of Poston's contemporaries observes, "We have had to suffer a lot of indignities because of our color. God only knows how many brilliant minds have been squashed. When God was giving out brains, He gave them to white *and* black. For many years, few people believed that. We were supposed to be inferior or subhuman. Ted suffered a great deal because he was black. He had all the amenities that he needed and he was quite at home with anybody. But, as he so often said himself, inside he had been crushed because his skin was black. In his stories, the teachers themselves were prejudiced. A black teacher didn't know any better than to give a light-skinned Negro child a position in a play that should have gone to a black child" (MDW). Another comments, "Ted is showing in these stories that he had a broad and deep cultural education in his segregated school. Ted was bright and he took advantage of it. He thought about things others didn't. His mind was way above ours. He was a mature person mentally from the time he was a little boy" (JKB).

Interviews of people in the stories and of others who knew Ted Poston as a child make up an oral history that portrays the observant journalist-in-the-making; documents the idiom and way of life of small-town Kentucky African American people in the early 1900s; and shows how they dealt with their surroundings, retained their self-respect, used their talents, and simply enjoyed life. The reader cannot presume that the stories are strictly autobiographical. Henry Lee Moon states that Poston was known as the "Great Embellisher." Poston made changes from life to fiction in order to entertain as well as to instruct.

During his first six years, 1906–1912, Ted Poston was nurtured in an educated, religious, stable family, "quality colored folks" of the community. His father, Ephraim Poston—whose name means "very fruitful"—from Clarksville, Tennessee, married Mollie Cox, age sixteen, three days before Christmas 1887. In July 1888 the first of their eight children, Frederick Douglass Poston, was born. Robert Lincoln came in February 1890; Ulysses Simpson, or "General," in 1892; Ephraim, Jr., in 1893; the first daughter, Roberta, on 9 July 1895. Sometime before the 1900 census, a sixth child was born who did not live. Lillian came 19 May 1903, and Ted brought the Postons' eighteen childbearing years to a close, arriving on Independence Day 1906.

Most black people listed on the census for 1900 were illiterate and worked as laborers or washerwomen, but Ephraim and Mollie Cox Poston could read and write and were employed as teachers. The family rented their house at 643 Hayes Street by 1895 and took out a mortgage to buy it for $1000, at 6 percent interest, on 2 January 1902. (In 1920 the house was renumbered as 809.) The original large, two-story structure burned during the 1940s and was reconstructed differently, but the basic foundation of the house extant is the same as in the Postons' day.

Frederick Douglass Poston was twenty-four during the summer of 1912, when most of Ted Poston's Hopkinsville stories take place. The 1910 census claims that by this time the former teacher and grocer had become a sailor. Ted therefore probably did not know his oldest brother well, but Father Ephraim described the life-style of upwardly mobile blacks and labeled Fred "naughty" in a verse encomium to Dr. Patterson T. Frazer, the president of the black Male and Female College in Hopkinsville.

> *"Since Frazer Came to Hopkinsville"*
>
> We students used to board around
>   In various families in the town;
> Had what we call a good ole time,
>   For boarding out we thought sublime,
> An' entering with a truant's gait,
>   Sometimes early and sometimes late. . . .
>
> Fred Poston was a naughty boy;
>   It seemed to be his only joy,
> While going to the common school,

To break or bend most every rule.
The teachers simply "wore him out";
They flogged and throgged him 'round about.

His parents picked up what was lef'
And sent him to the M. & F.,
But now Fred says he'll be a man
And in P. T. Frazer's steps he'll stan';
He goes and learns with free good will
Since Frazer came to Hopkinsville.

In 1912 Robert, B'Rob in the stories, was twenty-two; Ulysses, twenty; Eph, Jr., nineteen; Roberta, seventeen; Lillian, nine; and Ted, six. B'Rob took over the role of big brother that Fred had relinquished. "Eph [pronounced Eeph] Poston had one boy that was a genius, Robert. He went crazy; he thought all this modern stuff back in those days. He got in with the law. When times changed, I guess he helped bring it about," said Rozelle Leavell, who had been Ted Poston's shop teacher.

Robert and Ulysses Poston served in the army during World War I as sergeants, although they were soon demoted for being too militant for 1918. Briefly they helped their father publish a black newspaper, the *Hopkinsville Contender,* for which young Ted ran copy. The brothers took the *Contender* to Nashville and later Detroit, where in 1920 they met Marcus Garvey and were inspired to join his Universal Negro Improvement Association and assist him on his fine newspaper, *The Negro World.* Thus a part of the blossoming Harlem Renaissance, B'Rob met and married sculptor Augusta Savage. He took her back to visit Hopkinsville, where she enchanted Ted and his young neighbors, Charles Bronaugh and the Bacon children, as she showed them how to make masks of their own faces. She instructed them to spread Vaseline all over their faces, place two soda straws in their nostrils, then put wet mud over the Vaseline. When the mud dried, it made an exact three-dimensional replica of each one's face.

In the Postons' backyard was a stable. Ted "was a person with ideas, the kingpin who would start something and motivate the rest of us to want to do it, too," Bronaugh remembers. Ted connected a rope from the top of the barn to a tree next to Alex Lee Hopson's house and placed a tire on the rope. "We'd get in the tire and ride out of the barn, down—like on a chute or slide, and that was our pleasure."

Allison Williams recalls Ted's sleight of hand as they gambled up in the stable loft. "Pitty-pat was a little joked-up card game matching your cards. You deal five and have to come up with six, three pair. Everybody would throw in a nickel and whoever got out first would take the pot. That Ted was a character. He had a way of when he got nine nickels into a fifty-cent piece, he'd drop the fifty-cent piece through a crack in the floor. When they got ready to collect for the ten games, he'd say, 'Man, where *did* that fifty-cent piece go?' He'd go down and pick the coin up later."

Ted Poston says in the stories that his father was dean of men at the Kentucky State Industrial College for Negroes in Frankfort, but the Kentucky State Normal and Industrial Institute for Negroes (KNII) catalog for 1913–1914 lists him as an "instructor" in the "preparatory department." Father Ephraim commuted home every other weekend from the beautiful hillside campus beyond the city limits of Frankfort. The Louisville and Nashville Railroad had a stop at the campus on the interurban line, and Mr. Poston would board with a newspaper under his arm and his weather-beaten satchel in hand for the trip home to Hopkinsville. His children eagerly awaited him and so did all the black townspeople who wanted their disputes settled by the mild-mannered elder statesman who spoke slowly and with a slight stutter.

As Ted indicates in the stories, his parents were committed to education, and they took their Braxton nieces into their home so that they could get a good education before they moved on to Kentucky State. In 1914 Ephraim Poston registered ten students with the Hopkinsville Colored Board of Education: Robert, Ulysses, Ephraim, Jr., Roberta, Lillian, and Theodore Poston; Alberta and

Mary Belle Braxton; and Lee and Hester Broddie. Lydia Braxton Moten and Johnella Braxton Palmer, children of the Postons' cousin Leslie Braxton, say, "Uncle Poston was always giving people instructions on keeping their children in school and for a better life. He educated *his* children and he knew *we* had to be educated."

When Ted was ten, his mother "took sick" and by 11 May 1917 Dr. James S. May, the Postons' physician and neighbor across Hayes Street—a character in "Cousin Blind Mary"—was summoned to treat Mollie Poston for acute parenchymatous nephritis, an inflamed kidney, but she died on Memorial Day 1917. Eph, Jr., had died of a sarcoma on the neck in 1914. After Roberta finished at KNII, she took a position teaching at the one-room Oak Grove School, but she died of peritonitis on 14 April 1919.

Perhaps Lillian's greatest happiness after her mother died was simply sitting next to her father during his biweekly juridical sessions, as depicted in "The Birth of a Notion." When Father Ephraim went courting Susie Forrest in Paducah, Kentucky, in 1924, Lillian, who had suddenly dropped out of Kentucky State when another student passed her academically, went back to Hopkinsville to no future and was found wandering in her nightgown. She was taken to Western State mental hospital, where she died of pulmonary tuberculosis in 1927.

Thus, Ted Poston's happy childhood world fell apart during his adolescence. All of black Hopkinsville reeled when B'Rob succumbed to pneumonia aboard ship on his way home from a Marcus Garvey–sponsored Back to Africa mission to Liberia in March 1924. This string of deaths transformed Ted from a protected youngest child to a troubled but proud and independent youth. After his father remarried in 1924 and moved to Paducah, Ted roomed off and on in Hopkinsville with friends Reuben "Tack-Haired" Baker or Allison Williams until he finished Crispus Attucks High School in June 1924. But none of his stories document the "dark side of Hopkinsville" from the time Mollie Poston died. "After he got high school age, sixteen, Ted had to be a hustler because his family had deteriorated and Ted had to get it the best way he could. There wasn't nobody to give Ted nothin'" (AW).

Ted Poston is remembered by countless associates as an avid reader since childhood: "To my knowledge, Ted never had a complete set of schoolbooks in his life, but he always stood at the head of the class. He used to come here and study with me. My mother made a joke of it. She would say, 'I bought the books for *you*, and *Ted* makes all the good marks.' We had a bookcase in the corner. Ted would always have a book out and would lie on the floor there and read and read" (AW). "Ted was smart—jovial—he could tell jokes and things. But that never kept him from his books" (MQ). "He seemed to be a guy who was always a jump ahead of his fellow students and associates, without himself realizing it. It was known all over town that the whole family were book wizards. He was born with the mechanics which did not require him to study as hard as others. Yet he was always found with his head buried in some type of reading material, between his periods of study and funning. I have observed him to sit down and study for a period of only a few moments and remember more than the average student who had probably put hours into his study" (JTL).

"He was a go-getter. That's exactly the way I picture him. Whether it was something good or something bad, he was still in there to carry us on. Hell, he was investigating. It's human nature to want to know" (CWB). "I can recall Ted swimming. He was an expert. We all went to the Waterworks Dam. Ted would dive from the highest bluff down into the water 10 or 12 feet" (JTL). "I didn't know how to swim—and was standing on the dam. All of a sudden I felt myself flying through the air. I hit the water and Ted picked me up. He had tossed me up, then dived down and caught me" (CWB).

As Ted relates in the stories, the citizens of the dark side of Hopkinsville kept up with what was going on in the world by reading the newspaper.

"Some people read the *Nashville Tennessean,* but most people read the *Louisville Courier-Journal* because it was a liberal paper and it was delivered. Old Man Claude Brasher used to drive it around in a horse and buggy early in the morning." On the Attucks School corner, First and Vine, stood the water trough for that horse as well as for the horses pulling buggies and wagons in from the country on the Russellville Road (AW).

Although Hopkinsville was a town, it had a country atmosphere. On the Postons' street, also unpaved and with no cars, Alex Lee Hopson led a scout troop in drills at night.

Fifty acres of land on North Main Street composed Means' pasture, where in the stories Ted plucked dew apples. "Everybody in town had a cow and if they didn't have a big yard, they would graze their cows at Means' pasture. They'd pay a kid twenty-five cents a week to drive the cow out there in the morning and back in the evening. That was a whole lot of money then because minimum wage was fifty cents a day" (AW).

As the stories show, people had smokehouses for preserving meat—refrigerators were still far in the future. "Hog-killing season started in November, whenever the first of the really cold weather came. People would soak the pork, then salt it for so many months, then they would hang it up and smoke it. Zero degree weather is good hog-killing weather" (JKB).

"William Duncan used to go out to the garden at the mental hospital to pick watermelons, just as Ted did. He came walking back—three miles—and not even come in the house to get a knife to cut them open but would break them open on the back porch step and sit down and eat them hot," Mary Duncan Wilson claims.

In "Knee Baby Watkins," Poston shows how the black kitchen workers bragged about their white folks. He tells "how we thought in those days about the people descended from house slaves. We thought that those who worked in the house told on those who were out in the field. We called them 'white folks' niggers'—people who would go and tell everything. We didn't like that kind" (JKB).

Rat Joiner's children explain that Billy Goat Hill smelled pungent when they were growing up because of the stockyards. Today it is a pleasant little street above the L. & N. tracks that carry freight trains between Chicago and Florida. Down the south side of the hill is the stockyard, where cattle are still collected for shipment to Chicago. Stock auctions are held only on Tuesdays and Thursdays, and the Joiners say that those are the only days that they catch a whiff of the former barnyard aroma now. "If Rat lived there, he had to be tough to take the teasing that went with it" (JKB).

Saturday's movie-going, as Poston shows, was a highlight of the week for Hopkinsville's black children. "We tried our best to finish our work—sweeping the backyard, raking the front yard, sweeping the walk, scrubbing the back porch, the front porch and the kitchen, for which Aunt Becky gave me and my brother a dime apiece—by 10:00 A.M. so we could be at the picture show when it opened," says Allison Williams. "Then we had to be home by 6:00 P.M. We spent five cents for the movie, two cents for the candy-coated peanuts, three cents for salted peanuts, and with that we would see the show three times." Marcus Quarles spent his whole five cents on popcorn.

An old man, a Civil War veteran, also went to the show every Saturday morning. "He put his uniform on with three or four medals. He'd stand up in the middle of the show and holler at the screen, 'Look out, there's an Indian coming up on you. Look out, man. He's right behind you'" (AW).

Tapper Johnson, the first black movie projectionist in town, lived on Billy Goat Hill near Rat Joiner. He was responsible for enriching the local children once when he accidentally broke the projector and a large amount of mercury rolled across the floor into a corner of the projection booth and it stuck together. Williams says, "When you touch it, it splits apart. Oh, that stuff was heavy. Ted was in on this. We rolled the mercury into a half-pint mayonnaise jar. We found that if you rub a penny to get it warm, then the mercury will stick to the penny and make it look like a dime. For a while, we had a heck of a lot of dimes."

While Saturdays were devoted to movies, Sunday's ritual included a trip to the L. & N. station. Marcus Quarles says, "Sunday morning we went to Sunday School, church, ate dinner, then swimming or boat riding up and down the Little River until 5:00 P.M. At 5:00 P.M. everybody would be at the L. & N. station to see the '51' come in. It was a local that stopped all up and down the line. But that train platform was full. To find anyone, you'd go to the train station at 5:00 P.M. We'd watch people get on and off. That was our routine every Sunday. After the '51' came in, we would go to BYPU, Baptist Young People's Union. The show and the '51' were a ritual. Talk to young people now and they burst out laughing. 'That's all you had to do? Look at a train?' When World War I started, we watched the soldiers load up and leave on that train."

Although discussing skin color in the black community was taboo, most black people considered dark skin undesirable. Light-skinned Allison Williams illustrates how subtly such inclinations developed in his own family: "Grandma would wake us up in the morning to the sound of coffee beans grinding in an old-fashioned hand-grinder held between her knees. But she wouldn't let us children drink coffee. She'd say, '*You* can't drink that coffee. It will make you black!'" It was an unconscious assumption that the light-skinned "high yallers, like Ed Glass, were thought to have more business sense than black blacks" (AW).

Mrs. Nixola Green, the leading social arbiter and leader of the Blue Vein Society in Ted Poston's fictional black community, is probably modeled on the fair-skinned teacher Mrs. Fannie Bronston Postell. Mrs. Postell was Poston's principal in elementary school and his French and Latin teacher in high school. The most uppity of Hopkinsville's black community, she was nonetheless a more sympathetic character than the fictional Mrs. Green.

Poston defines the criteria for membership in blue-vein societies in "The Revolt of the Evil Fairies." At the turn of the century, many mulattoes took pride in having skin so fair that they could distinguish the blue veins beneath it. Charles W. Chesnutt showed its unfortunate effects in novels such as *The Wife of His Youth* and *The House Behind the Cedars*. Jennie Knight Baker, who looks white, didn't know of any secret Blue Vein Society when she and Ted were growing up, "but I've heard of it. Miss Mary Gill says there was definitely a trend toward the light-skin joining off together. But there wasn't that trend in my family to discriminate against dark skins or to feel differently because of color. I don't know any families in town who felt superior for that reason. That's why I am surprised at Ted [in these stories]. My brother was darker than I am, or than anyone else in our family, and he had some of that feeling toward me. But I couldn't worry about that; it wasn't my doings. [Miscegenation] was something going around before we came. You just have to live it out after you're born. Live life the best way you can."

Even though Ted Poston mocks Mrs. Nixola Green for her airs, the real-life Mrs. Postell, J. T. Lynch recollects, was "very fond of Ted Poston because he was such an outstanding student. Passing her room at Attucks High School, he would poke his head in the door and they would exchange a few words in French or Latin." Mrs. Postell, it is true, was "snooty, a haughty-type person, but she was not a socialite, like Ted's Mrs. Nixola Green. Mrs. Postell didn't belong to any 'society' except church. She was into the improvement of kids. She was thorough and wanted to see that they got the best education they could get. Look at Ted: he is a product of her teaching" (JKB).

Dr. Cassett and Mayor Haslett in the stories are probably modeled on the popular physician and mayor Dr. Frank H. Bassett, Sr., a Democrat. Christian County historian William T. Turner relates that black men first got the vote in 1870 and were "staunch Republicans because they considered Abraham Lincoln their savior. But that changed in 1920—the first year black women could vote—because of Dr. Frank Bassett, who treated black people with respect." Allison Williams says that "Dr. Bassett was a handsome white politician with a big, black mustache. He wore a gold chain across his chest, a mark of most politicians, rich men, at that time. For poor people Dr. Bassett would do favors, like going out in the country on house calls. When people couldn't get another doctor, Dr. Bassett went. That was before the time of welfare. If the poor people wanted *anything*, they went to Dr. Bassett."

"December 7, 1917, it started snowing. Western Kentucky was inundated with snow until March 1918" (WTT). "That was the winter of the great flu epidemic. During the very cold weather, Dr. Bassett went to the mines and bought a carload of coal and brought it in to where the railroad track crosses Fourth Street and he distributed it to the poor people so they'd have heat—so they'd *have* fuel. He was just nice, and it got to be that municipal jobs were thrust on him. He was mayor, county court clerk. Just anything he ran for, Dr. Bassett got it" (AW). Jennie Knight Baker tells of another of Dr. Bassett's acts of kindness: "We had a small house that my parents let me collect the rent on. A little blind man, Charlie Magahee, lived in it. He played music on a hand organ, down at the courthouse, and every week Dr. Bassett gave him the rent money—$1.25. That was my spending money."

Since Dr. Frank H. Bassett, Sr., was mayor of Hopkinsville and blacks were not "invisible" to him, it is possible that he initiated a Liberty Stamp Contest for Colored, as Ted Poston relates in "Rat Joiner Whips the Kaiser." The *Hopkinsville Kentuckian* carried a six-column ad on 6 June 1917 for "A Liberty Bond in Every Home: It is a Certificate of Patriotism." So Dr. Bassett would have been trying to involve the black citizens in a patriotic cause.

The model for the successful entrepreneur Mr. Fertilizer Ferguson in "High on the Hog" was probably Wick Mumford, who had a knack for making money. Wick Mumford sold ice cream in Hopkinsville starting about 1910, historian Turner reports. Then Mumford got into the sanitation business as well. "That got to be a joke. Whenever one of the Mumfords went by on his sanitation wagon with the big cans on the back on his outhouse-cleaning mission, people would say 'Here comes the ice cream man,' and his smelly wagon was called 'the ice cream truck'" (AW).

The youngest in his family, Ted Poston learned from his older siblings, then in turn taught the neighbor children younger than he. Charles Bronaugh, for example, trotted along behind the older boys.

One thing Ted taught me was how to steal a chicken. Ted would come from Hayes Street through the Bacons' backyard, by the Sanctified Church, and pick me up; then we'd go get Allison, and Willie Leverett, or Jason Bowles, or Ed "Skeeter" Bowles. We would go down to the Waterworks Dam with a fishhook so we could get somebody's chicken along the way. We'd put a grain of corn on the fishhook and catch the chicken. With a fishhook in his mouth, the chicken can't holler and he can't squeal or make any noise where you can hear it. And you just pull him on in. We'd take him down to the dam, dig a hole, build a fire and put the chicken in with his feathers still on; then we'd go swimming and make a day of it. Ted showed us how to do it.

The feathers came off real easy after it was cooked, the skin with it. We'd have salt and pepper, drink the clean creek water. You been swimming all morning and you didn't have any lunch? Oh, that was good. (CWB)

Stealing a chicken was only one option for a lazy summer afternoon. "Back up the Little River we had a lean-to," Allison Williams says.

Ted and I would leave home early in the morning with our fishing poles and bacon and eggs. We'd take them three miles up the tracks, swim across the river, and spend the whole day swimming. When we got tired, we'd cook our dinner. We didn't need a skillet. We'd use the lid from a five-gallon tin of lard. There were a lot of cornfields up there. We'd go get ourselves corn and cook it over a fire; kill a chicken, cook that, fish.

In those days, corn was fifteen cents a dozen; two dozen for a quarter. A man came by all summer with a pushcart, selling that corn. Mama bought two or three dozen ears every morning. Then the police got that man on the Pembroke Road and gave him sixty days. It turned out he had been going up near our swimming place with that pushcart, picking corn from different farmers' fields and selling it. It was delicious. And he did that all summer before anyone knew it was stolen.

We used to make our own toys, bows and arrows, and slingshots. For our fishing poles, we got wrapping cord and saved it all winter, then put beeswax on it and tied it to reeds that we had cut in the fall and that hardened up over the winter. That beeswax would waterproof the wrapping cord. (AW)

Poston's most anthologized story, "The Revolt of the Evil Fairies," suggests that Poston did not "get the girl" because his skin was too dark. Little Sarah Williams is based on the love of Poston's childhood, a doctor's daughter, Mary Duncan, who claims that she was "a paper doll fool" (MDW). Poston cut paper dolls out of his mother's magazines to give to her. Jennie Knight Baker, a member of Mary's clique, the Big Six, confirms, "Ted was just wild about Mary. He'd let everybody know he was in love with her. And we knew it by instinct. She was a darling person, a lovely girl, and Ted just adored her. That was the biggest romance that we had in our group. The others were just sort of palsy-walsy."

But Mary's father, Dr. James Duncan, Sr., as dark-skinned as Ted, disapproved of the romance. If anything, Mary was an obedient daughter. Dr. Duncan objected to the Postons' "mental instability, a weak strain in the family. And genius is so close to insanity" (MDW). Many years later, in 1941, after Mary had been married to handsome, dark-skinned Clifford Wilson since 1928 and borne five children and Ted had "made it" in journalism and was settled in Washington as head of the Negro News Desk at the Office of War Information, he looked Mary up to see if there was finally any chance for them. When she told him why her father had disapproved of him, Poston snorted, "Leave it to your father to think of genetics!" As for the two of them then, Mary at age seventy-five recalls, "For us, it was just too late, too late."

Rat Joiner, whose real name was Theodore Roosevelt Joiner, is the hero of *The Dark Side of Hopkinsville*. The nickname came as part of normal nomenclatural teasing. When he was young, Joiner's peers thought that he resembled a mouse. "Mouse" became "Rat" when he grew older. "I believe that's why they held that name to me. And some of the lighter boys called me 'Shady.' Yes, ma'am, we had a lot of fun out of the boys" (TRJ). Rat Joiner was considered the physical arbiter of dissensions among black youths, just as Eph Poston was oral arbiter for black adults. Yet Rat Joiner's ripostes and mental machinations in the stories seem to lead to the conclusion that the system tries to program blacks never to win. Rat Joiner compared his own boyhood life-style with Ted Poston's:

> I was pretty fast on the school ground and I ruled him. I don't guess you might say he was running around on the school ground, playing, laughing, jumping, turning his fists like I was. That's the onliest difference between us. I was a pretty fast boy back in them days. I'd walk so fast I'd trip my own self. I won't say Ted didn't play like other boys, but he wasn't just *rough* like *I* was. I could just as quick run up the side of your head and then turn around [friendly] and say, "C'mon, let's go!"
>
> The way the teacher would punish us boys back in them days is if we done something in school, they'd set us right in front, there, with a gang of girls, and the boy would be ashamed to hold his head up. He'd just sit there so ashamed. Now, *these* days, that's where a boy wants to *be,* with the girls. (TRJ)

The two black Theodore Roosevelts, Poston and Joiner—one tall, one small—were both spunky like the president for whom they were named. But in 1983 Joiner asserted,

> Ted's daddy was a schoolteacher and them schoolteachers *make* their children get their lessons, you know. And Ted had a *goal.* It was to make something of himself. *I* didn't like school so much. I went to school twelve years and I just wanted to stop frettin'. Course I missed passing three times. I stopped in the ninth grade. Thirty-five and forty-five in one room. The teacher didn't have time to go from one to the other and learn 'em anything. On the blackboard she would write a whole string across starting at the end of the room and going to that door there and you call that algebra? I said to myself, "Great day, whooee, gracious! I don't know my fractions and you go telling

me algebra!" You see what I mean? I was just ignorant. Old Ted had a better gift than I had. I didn't have none.

I remember a club at school. We had a motto—I never *will* forget it: "Tonight we launch; where *shall* we anchor?" I launched here, but I anchored here, too, no further than right here [on Billy Goat Hill]. When Ted passed, I said to myself, "One of my old school buddies died and left me back." There's few of us living now. (TRJ)

At Ted Poston's funeral in January 1974, the *Louisville Courier-Journal* reporter observed how empty Virginia Street Baptist Church seemed. Few modern citizens on the dark side of Hopkinsville remembered Ted Poston or knew of his accomplishments. In December 1984, Rat Joiner and his wife of sixty-one years died within a week of each other. They had raised ten children and at their deaths 312 descendants filled the church. The Postons left no descendants. But in *The Dark Side of Hopkinsville,* both these adventurous black children of the early twentieth century anchored permanently.

Brackets in the stories enclose material deleted by Ted Poston in revision, which the editor has chosen to restore in this edition.

THE DARK SIDE OF HOPKINSVILLE

1

MR. JACK JOHNSON AND ME

I don't know who was really to blame, unless it was Mr. Jack Johnson or B'Rob (my brother Robert Abraham Lincoln Poston). Surely it wasn't me. And if you doubt it, you can ask Knee Baby Watkins; because, as Grandma Hettie would put it, I sure learned him after it was all over.

It all started that summer when B'Rob came back from waiting tables on the excursion boats up on Lake Erie. He had already finished Kentucky State Industrial College for Negroes (where Papa was Dean of Men) and most everybody in Hopkinsville, Kentucky, agreed that he was "the smartest of all them Poston boys." And now he was going to Princeton, way up there in New Jersey.[1]

[On his first day back home, B'Rob had found a can of Palmer's Skin Success ("guaranteed to give you a light complexion in just seven days") in our bathroom, and I couldn't understand what he got so excited about. Then when he marched into the back bedroom, he found Sister Lillian heating up an iron comb to straighten Sister Roberta's hair.

["Neither of you have any pride of race," he said in that precise tone of voice he had picked up on those Lake Erie pleasure boats. "Getting *white* in seven days, indeed! And you there, burning up your sister's perfectly good hair with that pressing iron. I'm ashamed of you both. Don't you realize how pretty you are just as you ARE?" (He was way ahead of the Black Panthers.)

1

[Both of them looked at B'Rob as though he were crazy, and Sister Lillian picked up the iron and calmly went on with what she was doing. I still didn't know what all the shouting was about, but anybody who could shout at Roberta and Lillian without getting bopped over the head just HAD to be an ally of mine. And I felt that B'Rob liked me better than either of them anyhow. At least, he spent more time with me that weekend than he did with anybody else, and I enjoyed every minute of it, even if he *was* always asking me questions.]

Before B'Rob had showed up, it had been a pretty tough summer for me all around. What with Mama and Papa teaching summer school up in Frankfort, and with all the rest of my brothers hopping bells, waiting table and redcapping all over the country to get enough money to improve the education they had already received at Kentucky State, I had been left alone with Grandma Hettie, Sister Roberta and Sister Lillian—the only man in the house. And being the man of the house can be pretty rugged—when both of your sisters are bigger than you, and you are only six years old.

B'Rob seemed very pleased when he found out that I was already reading the *Louisville Courier-Journal*. (And I saw no reason to tell him that I really didn't understand half the words everybody thought I did.) He was elated when he asked me what I knew about Mr. Theodore Roosevelt, for whom I was named.

"He led the Rough Riders up San Juan Hill and whipped Cuba," I told him promptly, "and them Rough Riders was colored men, all riding big black horses."

[Of course, I'd been tempted to ask B'Rob a question which had been bothering me for years. Why did Mama and Papa let Roberta's sixth grade teacher who named me, put her husband's name in there too? Didn't they know what Rat Joiner, Tack-Haired Baker, Knee Baby Watkins and the rest of my classmates in the Booker T. Washington Colored Grammar School would do to me if they ever found out that my full name was Theodore Roosevelt Augustus Major Poston, and that my initials spelled "TRAMP"?]

B'Rob was less pleased when I told him that our teachers insisted that the South was never defeated in the War Between the States, but was "overwhelmed by the foreigners and carpetbaggers who swarmed out of dens of evil up North."

But in spite of being pretty mad on hearing this, he kept his voice steady and his temper calm as he explained to me:

"In the first place, it was called the Civil War. And in the second place, the South *was* defeated. The only mistake the North made was to refuse to fight by chickadee rules—that is, not only knock them down, but *stomp* them. The South, you see, never really stopped fighting. And if we don't watch out, they just might win the Civil War yet."

And then he asked me what I knew about Nat Turner. I had never heard of him, so B'Rob told me about him. He said that this Nat Turner, a slave down in Virginia, was a real touch-hog. (You know: "Don't touch that hog or he'll root you.") And Turner secretly got all the other slaves together and made a plan to take care of all the white folks by chickadee rules.

"And he might have gotten away with it too," B'Rob added with a kind of funny smile, "if one of the high yellow house slaves hadn't gone squealing to the white folks on the very night set for the insurrection."

(Personally, I could see Mrs. Nixola Green, leader of the secret Blue Vein Society in Hopkinsville, doing just that.)

And, B'Rob added with a wide grin, "Some people say that Nat Turner is the reason that white folks in Virginia are *whiter* than all other white folks. They got that way when they heard what he was planning to do to them."

And then he asked me how well I could take care of myself. How was I at wrestling? Could I box?

"Pretty good, I guess," I told him. "I can whip anybody my size and age in the whole Booker T. Washington Colored Grammar School. Anybody, that is, except Rat Joiner of Billy Goat Hill. And can't nobody, naturally, beat Rat Joiner."

"Anybody," B'Rob corrected me, but I could see that he was pleased.

The question of Jack Johnson didn't come up until B'Rob's last day at home. Mama had come down from Frankfort to see him off, and she and Mrs. Priscilla Tandy were sitting on our front porch fanning, while B'Rob and I were talking in the yard chair just below them.

"What do you know about Jack Johnson?" he asked me, and I proudly started telling him, "He's the heavyweight champion, and he—" when Mrs. Tandy cut in.

"If you ask me," she began, although nobody had, "I don't think nothing of that Jack Johnson. Any self-respecting Negro who goes around marrying white womens ain't got no business being champion of nothing."

And I was a bit upset when I looked up at the porch and saw Mama nodding in agreement. (Because Mama never intervened in her children's discussions—except, maybe to correct our grammar.)

So B'Rob changed the subject right then and went on talking about something else. But before we all went down to the L. & N. Station that evening to see him off, he took me aside down by the stable.

"Ted," he told me quite seriously, "Jack Johnson is heavyweight champion of the *whole world*—not just the colored people. And they haven't been able to find any *white* Rat Joiner who can whip him. What I'm saying is this: he's the best in the world, and that's what I expect you to be. No matter what they might tell you down here, you are just as good as *anyone,* and I expect you *never* to forget it. Now I'm not telling you to go out and pick fights just for the sake of fighting, but I don't expect you to take *anything* off *any*body. Because if you can whip anybody your size and age in your school, you can whip anybody your size and age anywhere, no matter what his color is. Just remember that." [2]

I was listening to him all right, but at the moment I was still mad at Mrs. Tandy for not letting me tell B'Rob what I knew about Jack Johnson.

Of course I had never met Mr. Johnson personally, and so he was probably unaware that I was the only member of my First Grade Class to whom he had given two birthday presents. Because my birthday was July Fourth.

The first came on my fourth birthday in 1910, when Johnson caught up with that great big peckerwood, Jim Jeffries, in Reno and whipped him to a faretheewell to become heavyweight champion of the world. And exactly two years later he celebrated my sixth birthday—just a few weeks before B'Rob's short visit home—by fighting so close to chickadee rules with another cracker named Jim Flynn that the sheriff in Las Vegas had to stop the fight on a threat of locking Johnson up for assault and battery.

Of course, our local paper, the *Daily Kentucky New Era,* didn't carry a word about the Flynn fight, so we didn't hear about it until the Pulitzer Prize–winning *Louisville Courier-Journal* arrived by mail three days later. It seemed they didn't care how many "White Hopes" Johnson stomped. They carried the story right on the front page.

Well, I was undisputed boss of the Younglove-Hayes Street Boys and champion of everybody but Rat Joiner at the Booker T. Washington Colored Grammar School. But there was no young white tad in my neighborhood to prove that I could whip *anybody* my size and age, regardless of his color. It was frustrating. And it would probably have remained that way if the Rex Theatre had not booked a movie named "Ambush."

We heard from Tapper Johnson, our colored motion picture projectionist, that Mr. Stonewall Jackson Bolton, the manager of the Rex, had tried to turn "Ambush" down after he and Tapper and Mr. Max Kaplan, the owner of the Rex, had seen the preview the week before it was to run.

"How do you expect the glorious South to rise again," Mr. Bolton had asked, "if you keep showing these pictures where even the Indians are kicking white folks around?"

But Mr. Kaplan over-ruled him, and we all saw it at the Rex the next Saturday morning. And Saturday afternoon and Saturday night, too. After all, we had paid our nickels.

5

It was during the fifth showing that the whole thing worked itself out in the mind of Big Chief Geronimo Poston. I knew exactly where I'd find my group of young white tads to help me prove I could live up to the tradition of the great Jack Johnson.

Naturally, it would have to be at the swimming hole right under the dam of the City Reservoir. All the white boys, and all of us, used the swimming hole—separately, of course—and there were strict social traditions protecting its use. The procedure was simple. Them that got there firstest got the pool. And they held it until the other side came up with the mostest. And the firstest would then decide that they had had enough swimming and would quietly take their leave while the mostest took over. It worked that way for either side.

But I decided to change all that. Why should we allow them to use our swimming hole at all, I asked myself.

I put my plan into action the next morning, after all of us had run home from Sunday School, changed our clothes and headed for the swimming hole. All of the Younglove-Hayes Street Boys were on hand.

We assembled at the rock quarry, just round the bend in the Little River and parceled out our tasks. First, we sent Reaching Pete, who really didn't belong to our gang, but who could steal anything light enough to lift, to filch the clothes of the ten young white kids who were already frolicking in the swimming hole.

Reaching Pete was back in minutes with practically every stitch of clothing they had left beside the dam before they went in the water. We soaked each garment in the muddy water and tied each piece into as tight a knot as we could, before Reaching Pete sneaked the whole pile back to where he had found it. And then we went into action.

The little white tads were belly-busting, skeeting water, ducking each other and having a grand time when somebody looked up to the left bank of the river and saw ten black braves, headed by Little Chief Knee Baby Watkins, standing with folded arms and unsmiling faces, looking down at them.[3]

To a man, they broke for the right bank, only to look up and see ten more black braves, commanded by Big Chief Geronimo Poston gazing silently down at them, over folded arms.

The little white tads screamed and went swimming and scrambling down the river only to be confronted by Squawman Fat Alex Brooks and his black warriors spread across the neck of the Little River bend, arms folded, faces impassive.

Then they really panicked and rushed back to the foot of the dam where they huddled in terror (just like the white settlers in "Ambush" when the redskins caught them crossing the river on the way West).

But then one little red-headed Irish kid that I had never seen before (it turned out he was from Chicago and was visiting Hopkinsville relatives for the summer) detached himself from the huddle and walked toward the right bank, waving his white drawers as a flag of truce.

"Ugh," said Big Chief Geronimo Poston, motioning him to come to the bank and parley.

I had to say one thing for that little red-head; he didn't seem scared like the others. He took his time and crawled back into his pants before he straightened up and said his bit.

"All right," he said, "you got us out-numbered and surrounded, and you could beat us up with no trouble at all. But that wouldn't prove nothing but that you got the mostest. So why don't you pick one of yours to fight one of ours and settle the whole business thataway. Then, win, lose or draw, we'll go on home and leave the swimming hole to you all."

Big Chief Geronimo Poston instantly thought back to King Arthur and the Round Table and to Sir Lancelot, and grunted, "You got your treaty. Pick your man."

And the spunky little tad said, "I'll fight for us."

Of course, I could hardly wait to meet him on the field of honor.

He returned to his side, and I called my black braves from across and down the river and explained the treaty. There was some grumbling among our Blackfoot Indian tribe, but in the end they accepted it.

So after the little white tads had been permitted to unknot their

7

wet clothes and put them on, everyone gathered in a wide circle with me and the little red-head in the center. (His name was Aloysius.)

I held up my fists, arms bent at the elbow in the style of Jack Johnson, and the tournament was on.

I poked out my left in a Sam Dixon feint and prepared to bring a roundhouse right to my opponent's jaw, but somehow it never connected. I found myself sitting flat on the rocky grass and looking up at *two* red-heads named Aloysius!

I knew there had been an accident. I must have slipped or something. I scrambled up, arms flailing and waded in, all science to the wind. But somehow, there I was, on the grass again, face forward this time, having plowed a small furrow with my chin as I fell.

Nobody could ever call a Poston "yellow"—for several reasons. But when I went down the fifth time, I sat there for a minute to think things over. And when I looked up, it was to see this runty little Aloysius holding out his right hand, and saying,

"Shake. No hard feelings. Okay?"

I don't remember whether I shook his hand or not. I don't even remember when the triumphant little white kids took their leave. The first thing I remember was hearing Knee Baby Watkins laughing fit to bust, and pointing at me and saying,

"Look down there at old Big Chief Geronimo Poston. Who would think that a little old white runt like that could scalp him?"

That brought me to my feet in an instant, and I caught that fleeing Knee Baby and wiped up the whole dam area with him.

Of course the whole thing wasn't my fault. How could I have known that it was going to be *me*—and not Mr. Jack Johnson— who was going to meet up with a *white* Rat Joiner.

2

THE WEREWOLF
OF WOOLWORTH'S

The old Mays house, across the street from us in Hopkinsville, was empty for years because, folks said, it was haunted. I heard my sister Roberta tell some of her visiting classmates from Kentucky State Industrial College for Negroes that Mrs. Mays had come up missing one morning, and that her husband, one of our colored railroad brakemen, told everybody that she had run off with one of those city slickers who came to Hopkinsville with a minstrel.

"And she *was* pretty sassy," Roberta said.

But a couple of months later, when Mr. Mays up and quit his good brakeman's job and left town, it seems some people started doubting that his wife had actually run off after all. Then Grandma Hettie and Mrs. Arabella Jones, her childhood friend from the days of Reconstruction, began to hint that they sometimes heard strange noises from the old house, although it was still empty at that time.

Then one night, when Mama had persuaded Papa to go with her to the Wednesday Night Prayer Meeting at the Virginia Street Baptist Church, Grandma Hettie indulged herself in one of her favorite past-times, which was telling scarey stories to my sisters Roberta and Lillian.

"I don't like none of them funny noises I hears coming from that old Mays house on moonlight nights," she said. "One night last week I could hear somebody's feet running like everything, and then I hears this voice—didn't hardly sound human—and it was screaming like somebody was chasing somebody with a axe. Like to scare me half to death. Then I hears moans and groans, just something pitiful. Ain't nothing wouldn't make me go in that old house nohow. Course, I ain't superstitious, and I don't believe in no ghosts, but I sure doesn't like them noises." And then Grandma Hettie sat there and sucked on her corncob pipe, shaking her head like she was mystified. Roberta and Lillian were mighty scared, too.

It was almost midnight when Grandma Hettie said slyly to my sister Lillian, "Girl, I think you done forgot to bring that wash in from that back clothes line. You best run right out there now, and get it before it mildews."

Lillian didn't dare to disobey Grandma Hettie. She knew perfectly well the old lady would just tell her, "I don't take no back-sass from no grandchildren nohow. Even if they is growing up girls. Get on out there fore I go up side your head." So, shaking in every bone and sinew, poor Lillian went out there to get that wash.

Well, as I heard the story years later, Lillian was running back so fast with that wash, that she clean forgot about the FRONT clothesline, and that line caught her up under her chin so sharply that her feet flew out from under her, and she fell on her elbows, scraping both of them to the bone. Mama was as mad as a hornet when she came back from church and found Dr. Moore binding up Lillian's elbows. But Grandma Hettie just kept on sucking on her corncob pipe and insisted she didn't know what on earth had made Lillian act so silly. But there was no more talking in our house about the old Mays place being haunted.

And shortly after that the Harringtons moved in and Jimmie Harrington and I got ourselves born. There were no other little white tads on our street right then, and Jimmie and I always did everything together. I think I must have been almost four years old before I began to realize Jimmie wasn't my real brother. We had been born on the same night, just hours apart. Mama and Maggie Harrington became bosom friends (and even I recall that Mrs. Harrington had quite a lot of bosom), having babies the

10

same age, and it was always "Mollie this" and "Maggie that," from then on.

Lillian once told me that one day Mama left me with Mrs. Maggie while she went over to Pembroke to visit an ailing friend.

"When I went across the street to get you," she said, "there was Mrs. Maggie nursing both of you at the same time. And you were sucking like mad on your side, and at the same time, trying to kick Jimmie's out of his mouth."

I doubt that ever happened, but Jimmie and I were always as thick as thieves and did just about everything together. We gathered lightning bugs in Mason jars as soon as we were big enough to chase them. We hunted crawdads in the basin of the cool water spring up on Lovier's Hill.[1] We stole peaches out of Mr. Crawford's orchard as soon as we learned how to climb a tree. And we choked over our first corn silk cigarettes behind the stable before we even went to school.

It must have been about a year before I started at the Booker T. Washington Colored Grammar School that I introduced Jimmie to the wonders of the Five and Ten. We had two of them in Hopkinsville: F. W. Woolworth and S. H. Kress. Jimmie didn't understand at first that you really didn't need money to take home some of the treasures of these vast emporiums. It didn't work out so well in the beginning because he was a bit clumsy. And on our very first foray one saleslady almost caught him trying to tuck a Little Louisville Slugger baseball bat down in his britches. I rescued him by quick thinking.

"He was just measuring it down his leg for size," I told the saleslady, but I wasn't so sure she believed me. We decided it would be wise to stay away from the Kress store for a while.

So a few days later Jimmie and I worked out the perfect strategy. We left home together and went downtown to Woolworth's which we then entered by separate doors. Then we converged on the counter we had agreed upon in advance, approaching it from opposite sides.

Since Jimmie was white, it was only natural that the saleslady

11

would wait on him first. And while he was pretending to consider the relative merits of a catcher's mitt and three hard rubber balls, I cleaned out the other side and scooted.

I was pretty good at that sort of thing. Even Rat Joiner admitted it. I heard him tell Tack-Haired Baker one day: "Ain't no two ways about it. That Ted Poston is the Werewolf of Woolworth's."

And then one morning, soon after our Woolworth coup, Jimmie and I woke up to find ourselves with two brand new neighbors. We saw them standing up on the corner of Hayes and Mechanic, right outside the grocery store which had been closed since Old Man Garnett had died some three weeks before.[2]

Jimmie and I slowly walked toward them, studying them with care as we drew near, and then somewhat stiff-legged, we circled them from both sides, and then surrounded them. I stuck my face right under the jiggling Adam's Apple of the tall, skinny, white-haired one, and demanded, "What's your name?"

"Karl Marx Whord," he said, backing into Jimmie.

"I'm Frederick Engels Whord," said the short dark-haired one, without being asked. "We're going to run this store here."

"Uncle Garnett left it to Father," continued Karl.

"Father is a Socialist; he don't believe in private property. He says it's Capitalism. He didn't want to take it, but Mother made him do it."

"Mother said nobody starves in a grocery store. She said if you can't sell the stuff you can eat it."

But I wasn't interested in economics or politics, so I broke up their gabble as soon as I could get a word in.

"You wanna wrestle?" I asked Karl.

"Or box?" said Jimmie hopefully, from behind him.

"Father is a Pacifist," he answered quickly. "He won't let us fight. He says the workers should do their fighting against the bosses. We got to unite."

"Mother ain't no pacifist," Frederick volunteered. "When Father gave ten dollars one time to his Socialist cell up in our hometown, which was Hartford, Connecticut, Mother hit him over the head with the empty skillet. She said there wasn't nothing ELSE to do with it since Father had given away our food money."

So Jimmie and I gave up in disgust. This kind of thing could have gone on all morning. So we took them on out to Means' Pasture with us so we could gather up the May apples before the sun dried the dew off the ripe ones.

But we had to admit later that our first impressions of Karl and Frederick were all wrong. For, within a week, they were full-fledged members of the Hayes Street Boys, which included Fat Alex Brooks next door, and little Skeeter Goines down the street, and they had fought very well in a skirmish with the Younglove Street Boys led by Knee-Baby Watkins.

And it was after that first skirmish that I learned the value of having white friends. Knee-Baby came down to Hayes Street under a flag of truce next day.

"You all ain't fighting fair," he complained. "You knew that Mama 'n'em was going to tell us we better not hurt them white boys. And ain't nobody telling them they can't hurt us. It ain't FAIR."

The upshot was that the Hayes Street Boys and the Younglove Street Boys got together—much to the disgust of Knee-Baby. But he didn't offer to fight me to see who was going to be the boss of the whole shebang. He KNEW.

But most of the time, Jimmie and I hung out with Karl and Fred, and our new-found friends had more ideas for getting something-for-nothing than Jimmie and I had ever thought of. It was Fred, for instance, who discovered that the melons in Old Man Johnson's melon patch, out by the Fair Grounds, were just getting ripe. He taught us that even the smallest of the melons, when it was ready to eat, would give out a hollow sound when you plunked it with your middle finger.[3]

We sure loved those melons, but this created a rather delicate situation for me, because Grandma Hettie had definite ideas about any Negro who went around eating watermelon in broad daylight. And her ideas were even stronger about little Negro tads who stole watermelons by moonlight.

But a real good general can't desert his troops, so after we stole the cantaloupes and watermelons that night, we ate them over in Jimmie's back yard.

And, best of all, Karl and Fred enjoyed our forays to the Five and Ten Cent Stores.

"Both Old Man Kress and Old Man Woolworth are capitalists," Karl explained solemnly, "so it is only fair that us workers should get ours any way we can." Neither Jimmie nor I knew a capitalist from a socialist, but it was fun hitting more than one counter at a time at the five-and-ten. That way you HAD to come up with something good.

And then the roof fell in on all of us, although we didn't know it until sometime later.

For Mr. Timothy Harrington, Jimmie's red-faced Irish Daddy, came home to stay for a while.

Now, although Mrs. Maggie was in and out of our house all the time with a "Mollie, could I borrow a cup of sugar (or an egg or a slab of fatback for my mustard greens)," her husband had never darkened our door. True, he wasn't home even as often as Papa and Mama. But there was another thing: on the few Sundays he was in town, he never rode in our buggy when Mama used to drop Mrs. Maggie and Jimmie off for Mass at the big stone Catholic church down by the post office, when we were on our way to the Virginia Street Baptist Church.

"I'll walk. I need the constitutional," Mr. Harrington always said.

He wasn't unfriendly, exactly. At least he was always grinning at everybody and telling jokes that made his big belly bounce up and down.

When anybody asked Mrs. Maggie where her husband was, she would say vaguely, "Tim's out counting votes." It took me a time to figure that out. And then I heard my grandma say, "that Tim Harrington must be worse at rithmetic than that Eph my Mollie done married. Seems like he's been counting votes for half a dozen office runners and ain't none of them ever come in smelling distance of no office winning, nohow. No matter HOW many votes he say he counted."

But Mr. Tim, he was always telling Papa about all the big politicians he was related to up in New York City. From the way he talked, Papa said, you would think they owned Tammany Hall, and Papa seemed to know what that was. And he used to love to brag about his rich relatives up in Boston. He said they were the Society leaders of the whole town. I heard Papa telling Mama about it one night, and then he leaned down under the dining-room table, where he knew I'd be reading my new book about Nick Carter, and he asked me:

"Ted, you are in the Harrington house often enough. Did you ever notice any lace curtains over there?"

But before I could answer, Mama shut him up with a stern, "Professor Poston!" and I never did find out what he was talking about.

So Jimmie and I didn't pay his father no mind that night when he came home for the week-end. With Fred and Karl, we were playing "Sitting Bull and General Custer" in our front yard, so they could get even. Usually we played Bronco Billy and his Negro sidekick, Pistol Pete, in my version of which Pistol Pete was the hero and Bronco Billy was HIS sidekick, and Fred complained when we played this. He said, "I'm tired of biting the dust; me and Karl get killed all the time." So that night, the Indians (Karl and Fred) wiped out General Custer (Jimmie) and his brave but wounded courier (me) escaped to take the sad news back to Washington.

Mr. Harrington was sitting on his front porch where he could see us playing. It was about bedtime when the game was over, so the victorious Karl and Fred went on up to the corner where they lived over the grocery store, and Jimmie went across the street to his house. I only noticed vaguely that his father stopped him and made him sit in the porch swing with him.

Next morning, I was surprised when Jimmie came over early, with his eyes all red as though he had been crying.

"Ted," he blurted out, "I can't play over here no more if Karl and Fred are here."

"Why not?" I asked, really puzzled.

"Well, my Daddy said they are Jews, and—" he began, but I cut him off.

15

"They ain't neither," I told him flatly. "They ain't nothing but white folks, just like you."

"Naw," Jimmie said miserably, hanging his head. "Daddy says they're Jews, and Jews is Christ-killers; they killed Christ."

"They ain't killed nobody," I started to protest, when Mama's voice, unusually sharp, from inside the house, cut me off.

"Jimmie Harrington, you come here," she ordered sternly.

"Yes'm, Mrs. Mollie," he said, wondering, with me, if we were going to get tanned for something. But Mama just spoke to him.

"Jimmie," she said seriously, "you go right back home to your house, and you ask your Daddy WHAT Christ was. You tell him I told you to ask him. You just say, 'What was CHRIST?' and you come right back here and tell me what he says."

"Yes'm," Jimmie said, and scooted across the street.

But he never came back—then, or ever. And that evening, when Karl and Fred and I were playing robbing a stage coach in our front yard, we could see Jimmie over there pretending to play by himself, but sneaking looks in our direction. He looked pretty lonely, and then soon he just quit playing.

I felt sorry for Jimmie, and I told Karl and Fred what his father had done to him. Neither one of them seemed as surprised as I had been. They just looked at one another for a minute, and then Karl said, "He did, huh." And we went on back to holding up the stage coach.

They left soon after that and went on up to the corner and to bed. I had no idea then that we all had spent our last week together. The following Wednesday, Mr. Harrington came home, bragging all the way from the L. & N. Station. It seemed that, at long last, he had counted votes for a winner, some man who was running for sheriff in a town near Louisville, and the man had paid him off by appointing him dog-catcher of the county.

Grandma Hettie had sniffed at Mr. Harrington's new job, but Papa told her, "It's not as small as it sounds, Granny. He will get twenty-five cents for every stray dog he takes in to the pound, and an energetic man can make a pretty penny if he puts his mind to it." Some months later we heard he had been *too* energetic, and people all over the county were up in arms about missing pets and hunting dogs. And when the sheriff's own two prize hound dogs turned up in the pound—delivered there by the new dog-catcher himself—Jimmie's daddy had to get out and start "counting votes" for someone else.

But at the time, he packed Mrs. Maggie and Jimmie up that very Wednesday night, and they took the Dixie Flyer out at nine-fifteen P.M. He had already arranged for Fertilizer Ferguson to pack up their stuff the next day and bring it up to their new home near Louisville, in one of his garbage wagons.

And, in addition to Jimmie's sudden departure, I received another blow at that time. Before the week was out, Mr. Whord, our reluctant grocer, had found a buyer, and, over the vigorous objections of Mrs. Whord, had sold out and made preparations to take his family back to Hartford and his Socialist cell.

I missed Fred and Karl, but Jimmie was my real boon coon, although he once boasted that he was older than I, having been born a few hours before midnight, on July third. I shut him up quick by asking,

"Yeah? Well who ever shoots off fire-crackers on YOUR birth-day?"

After he went away, nothing was ever quite the same.

3

KNEE BABY WATKINS

You couldn't exactly say that Knee Baby Watkins was sneaky. But we young tads who grew up with him had our own ideas about Knee Baby long before we all first entered the Booker T. Washington Colored Grammar School.

And there is no doubt that Knee Baby was the catalytic agent who precipitated the most disastrous social feud in the history of Hopkinsville, Kentucky.

The thing started out as a Knee Baby–inspired dispute between two respected members of our colored community, and ended up with some of our best quality white folks not speaking to each other.

But that was Knee Baby for you. We young tads knew him from way back.

There was the matter of his name, for instance. There was an unverified report around town that he was originally named Oswald Watkins, but none of us ever knew him as anything but Knee Baby.

He got the name quite simply: From the day he was born until he was at least five years old, Oswald Watkins simply refused to stand up and walk like everybody else—except on Sundays and Wednesdays. All the rest of the time he scurried around on his hands and knees.[1]

Nobody really knew how this came about, unless it was just pure cantankerousness on Knee Baby's part. But Mama blamed Mrs. Oceola Watkins, Knee Baby's mother, for it.

The words "progressive education" had never been heard of in the Booker T. Washington Colored Grammar School in those days. But Mama had her own ideas about mothers who spoiled their children.

"She's always telling people: 'Don't force him to do anything,' " I heard Mama tell Papa one night. "She says: 'I want him to make up his mind about things for himself. I want him to be independent.' "

(My Grandma Hettie looked around suspiciously at *me* while Mama was talking, so I just quietly slipped out of the room. For Grandma Hettie was not above bopping me over the head and saying: "That's for nothing, now look out." She was determined *I* wasn't going to be no Knee Baby Watkins.)

Other friends and neighbors of Mrs. Oceola shared Grandma Hettie's opinion, and they did what they could to try to correct the doting mother's indulgence.

There was the day, for instance, when Mrs. Oceola had to run over to Clarksville, Tenn., to comfort an ailing relative. And she left Knee Baby with Mrs. Arabella Jones, a contemporary of Grandma Hettie, who lived right across the street.

Well, Grandma was over there visiting that day when Mrs. Arabella was trying to make Knee Baby eat his supper.

"She had made a very good chicken soup," Grandma later told Mama, "and that little so-and-so wouldn't touch a drop of it. He just sat there glaring like a baby bull moose and refused to open his mouth.

"Well, I fixed him," Grandma Hettie said with satisfaction.

And I could attest to that. For it was me that Grandma Hettie called from the backyard that afternoon when an impasse had been reached in Mrs. Arabella's kitchen.

There sat Grandma Hettie and Mrs. Arabella on one side of the kitchen table, and Knee Baby on the other. And they were all glaring at each other. Grandma Hettie finally broke the silence:

"You run over home, Ted," she told me, "and get that new flit gun your Papa got to spray them tomatoes. Be sure you get that new one which he didn't use yet, and bring it right back here to me."

Naturally, I was back with the gun in record time. For one didn't tarry on errands for Grandma Hettie.

She took the flit gun without a word and walked over to the kitchen stove. While she fiddled around there, Mrs. Arabella got up nonchalantly and strolled over behind Knee Baby's chair. Grandma Hettie came back across the table and Knee Baby continued to give her glare for glare.

But suddenly Mrs. Arabella jabbed Knee Baby where-it-hurts-most with a sharp hat pin, and his mouth flew open so wide it seemed the top of his head was coming off.

But before he could get out his yell, Grandma Hettie brought the flit gun up into firing position and shot at least a pint of hot chicken soup down his gaping throat.

Knee Baby sputtered and choked and scrambled out of the chair and right under the kitchen table on his hands and knees. There was one thing you had to say about Knee Baby. He could get much swifter four-way action than an ordinary man could on just two legs.

Grandma Hettie and Mrs. Arabella just stood there saying nothing, although Grandma Hettie was hard put to keep from laughing.

Mrs. Arabella started to say something, but Grandma Hettie shook her head vigorously.

And sure enough a few minutes later, Knee Baby stuck his head out from under the table and looked around apprehensively. And, believe it or not, his tongue was going halfway around his face lapping up the rest of that chicken broth.

And when Grandma Hettie and Mrs. Arabella continued to maintain silence, Knee Baby slowly climbed up the rungs of the chair, shuffled into his seat at the table and drank every drop of the chicken soup that was left in his bowl.

Mrs. Oceola (who never knew what happened) couldn't get over it the next week.

"He *never* used to drink soup at all," she told Mama while visiting us one day, "but now he can't seem to get enough of it."

Grandma Hettie, who was quietly smoking her corn cob pipe in the corner, said nothing. But her lips were trembling around the smoke-stained pipe stem.

For Grandma Hettie had other ideas about Knee Baby too. Especially about his refusal to walk upright except on Wednesdays and Sundays.

"He ain't nothing but a show-off and a scrounger," she said. "I remember when he first started that foolishness.

"He stood up first just about the time that Ted here started toddling, and that Oceola made such a fuss about it that he knew right away he had a good thing. And when Pete (Mr. Pete Watkins, our colored Pullman porter) came back from his run that weekend, she screeched: 'You know what Oswald did last Wednesday? He stood up and *walked.*'

"Pete tried all that weekend to make him do it again. But the little so-and-so wouldn't budge. But when Wednesday rolled around next week and he heard them talking about it, he stood right up and walked again.

"And I know why he walks sometimes on Sundays too. That Oceola promises him an extra piece of sweet potato pie if he'll get up and show off for her Sunday visitors."

But we young tads who grew up with him knew that Knee Baby Watkins was a dangerous character—upright or on all fours. Especially on all fours when the old folks weren't looking.

Our parents used to take us by there on Sunday afternoons after church, for Mrs. Oceola admittedly made the best sweet potato pies in town.

The grownups usually went out on the front porch to talk about the new preacher or the lodge or something, and left us in the parlor with Knee Baby.

And neither he nor I could walk when Knee Baby first played his dirty trick on me.

He took one of his prettiest toys and lugged it out on the parlor floor. And then he scurried back and hid behind a big sofa chair. And when I crawled over and started playing with his little red firewagon, he sneaked up behind me and clouted me over the head with the shovel of a little beach sand set his Papa had brought him from the Louisville end of Mr. Pete's run.

My outraged and indignant scream brought Mama and Mrs. Oceola into the living room before I could get my hands on him (he could scamper faster than a thousand-leg bug), but Knee Baby wasn't one to let well enough alone.

Or else he didn't have any imagination.

For he was still playing that same dirty trick on unsuspecting visitors even after he had passed his fifth birthday. (And still scampering around on all fours.)

And that led us to think that maybe Knee Baby didn't have real good sense. For, as a five-year-old who should have known better, Knee Baby pulled his gambit on Rat Joiner.

It happened the first Saturday after Mrs. Roosevelt Alonzo Taylor Joiner, Sr., quit the Sanctified Church and joined the Virginia Street Baptist. So, figuring she should know her new church members, she came around to call on Mrs. Oceola Watkins that Saturday and brought her son, Rat Joiner, the pride of Billy Goat Hill, along with her.

As usual the grown-ups retired to the front porch, leaving Knee Baby and Rat in the parlor. Rat found himself fascinated by a wind-up three-car train which seemed to have been left accidentally in the center of the floor.

And while he was leaning over winding it up, Knee Baby emerged from behind the sofa and promptly bopped Rat over the head with a Little League Louisville Slugger bat which his Papa had brought back from a city of the same name.

How crazy could he get? Few grownups and no tads at all would dare bop Rat Joiner over the head when he wasn't looking.

But Knee Baby must have gotten the idea right away. For both Mrs. Oceola and Mrs. Roosevelt Alonzo Taylor Joiner, Sr., were surprised to see the front door fly open violently and Knee Baby shoot out *upright* in what was obviously an effort to break DeHart Hubbard's Olympic 100-yard dash record. And right behind him, brandishing the little Louisville Slugger bat, came Rat Joiner with blood (figuratively) in both eyes.

Both parents still had their mouths open, astounded, when Knee Baby cut the corner at Younglove and Mechanic Streets so sharply that his left ear picked up dust from the sidewalk.

And that was a turning point in more ways than one in the life of Knee Baby Watkins. For before Rat finally caught up with him and knocked him for a two-bagger some 18 blocks later, half of the people in Hopkinsville, Ky., had seen Knee Baby upright and active.

So there was no point in his scuttering around on all fours anymore. But he remained Knee Baby Watkins just the same.

And it was soon after that that even Mrs. Oceola lost patience with Knee Baby. First he accused her of "tricking" him by telling him it was Wednesday when it was really Thursday. And then he used this as an excuse to insist that he wasn't going to enroll in the Booker T. Washington Colored Grammar School that fall.

Mrs. Oceola paid him no mind when the time rolled around. She just took him by one hand and dragged him screaming the five blocks to the Booker T. Washington Colored Grammar School and pushed him down in a seat with everybody else.

But Mrs. Oceola really lost her temper when she got back home an hour later (after stopping to chat with Grandma Hettie and Mrs. Arabella Jones) to find Knee Baby hiding behind the overstuffed chair in the living room. He had sneaked out the back door while Miss Clara Willis, our First Grade teacher, was registering the rest of us and had scurried through Garnett's Alley to beat his Mama home.[2]

Mrs. Oceola took a firm stand at last. She went out in the back yard and cut a mulberry switch off a limb and brought it back in the house with her.

And every morning for the rest of that term, she placed Knee Baby in the middle of Younglove Street and fanned him towards Booker T. with that mulberry switch.

Not that Knee Baby went quietly, even then. He contested the issue every step of the way. And he became an alarm clock for the whole neighborhood. For the minute he got to the corner of Younglove and Mechanic each morning, he'd let out his unchanging yell:

"I don' WAN-NA go to 'cool (gasp) dis mawning!"

Every time Mama heard it, she would say: "Time to get up, Ted. There goes Knee Baby."

But Mrs. Oceola was determined, and it took her less than a year to break Knee Baby. By the beginning of the second term she only had to whip him to the corner of Younglove and Mechanic, and if she got up enough steam in that half-block run, Knee Baby would coast the rest of the way to Booker T.

So by the time we reached the second and third grades, Knee Baby Watkins was just another student, and—to the surprise of everyone—a pretty smart if rather evil student at that.

It was that quality of smartness and evilness which finally enabled him to set off the social feud between Mrs. Cecelia Coole, our English teacher, and Mrs. Rosa Coldweather, our history teacher, when we were all in the Fourth Grade.[3]

Mrs. Rosa and Mrs. Cecelia had been good friends for years and they had a lot in common. Both were high yallers who had been "raised" by quality white families in Hopkinsville. That is, both had taken care of the little white tads and had lived with the white families while they were going to school at the local Male & Female College for Colored.

And it was hard to tell who was most proud of her relationship with her personal white folks. Mrs. Cecelia was more restrained. She only occasionally mentioned Mrs. Evangeline Jones, daughter-in-law of Mr. Beauregard Jones, our leading Banker. But when she did, you got the idea that Mrs. Evangeline Jones was very special white folks indeed.

Mrs. Rosa was altogether different. Hardly a day ever passed in History class that she didn't find some excuse to bring up Mrs. Dr.

24

Cassett, the wife of Dr. Frank Cassett, a growing political power in our town.

And that is how the feud got started. For one morning when Mrs. Rosa was saying, as usual, "I was telling Mrs. Dr. Cassett . . ." Knee Baby cut in with:

"That ain't good grammar."

Mrs. Rosa was so shocked at the interruption that she almost dropped her pince nez glasses as her head snapped up.

"What did you say, Oswald Watkins?" she demanded sternly.

"I said it ain't good grammar." Knee Baby held his ground. But then retreating slightly under Mrs. Rosa's baleful glare, he added:

"Mrs. Coole said it ain't good grammar. She said a doctor is a doctor and a Missus is a missus, but that a missus don't get no right to be called Missus Doctor just because she married a doctor."

Mrs. Rosa turned sort of red, but she didn't pursue the subject further. Instead, she snapped: "If you knew your history lesson as well as you think you know everything else you'd be much better off."

And when she whipped five of us for whispering in class a half hour later, it seemed she bore down a little harder on Knee Baby.

But nobody knew that a feud was in the making until lunchtime came and Mrs. Rosa didn't take her little basket over to Mrs. Cecelia's room to eat lunch with her. Nobody remembered this happening before.

And next morning, Mrs. Rosa could hardly wait for us to get settled in our History class before she opened up on Knee Baby.

"It might interest you to know, Mr. Oswald Watkins," she told him, "that I just happened to mention your ignorant remark to Mrs. Dr. Cassett last night, and she said it was perfectly proper to address a doctor's wife as Mrs. Dr., and that it is done all the time in quality circles."

Knee Baby apparently had been waiting for this. For he said quickly:

"How she know? Mrs. Coole said Mrs. Cassett never finished

Belmont College like her Mrs. Evangeline did. How she know what's right?"

Now none of us had heard Mrs. Coole say anything like that in English class, although it was common knowledge among our parents that they almost had to burn Belmont College down to get Mrs. Dr. Cassett out of the freshman class.

But this was a matter between Mrs. Rosa Coldweather and Knee Baby and we weren't going to put our two cents worth in.

Anyway, Mrs. Rosa almost had apoplexy. And when Rat Joiner hit Knee Baby in the head with a spit ball a few minutes later, she whipped Knee Baby before she got around to Rat.

And she not only didn't eat lunch with Mrs. Coole that day; she didn't even speak to her when she passed her in the hallway.

But even then, the all-out feud might have been avoided if Mrs. Ophelia Owens hadn't got sick that day and Mrs. Rosa hadn't had to take us over for our Spelling class. And it was just her luck that Knee Baby drew the word "veterinarian" when it came his turn to spell and describe.

"V-e-t-e-r-i-n-a-r-i-a-n," said Knee Baby triumphantly. "That's what Mrs. Coole said Dr. Cassett is, a hoss doctor. Now a hoss doctor ain't like a folks doctor. He goes around treating hosses instead of people . . ."

Mrs. Rosa didn't wait to hear any more. She announced she had a headache and went and told Prof. P. Long, our principal, that she was going home for the day.

But later that evening, when Mrs. Ida Baker, Dr. Cassett's cook, stopped by to see Grandma Hettie, I found out Mrs. Rosa didn't go home at all. She went straight out to see Mrs. Dr. Cassett and told her what Mrs. Coole was supposed to be saying around town.

"Mrs. Dr. Cassett is very put out about it," Mrs. Ida Baker said, "and she said she's gonna fix Mrs. Coole and Mrs. Evangeline Jones too. She's gonna give a big tea next week and she ain't gonna invite Mrs. Evangeline to it.

"When quality white folks start falling out, it's time for us colored folks to look out."

26

Grandma Hettie was a little contemptuous of all quality white folks. She contended that no real quality ones were left around Hopkinsville.

"Huh," she snorted, "I remember all of them squirts and their grandpappies before them. And all of 'em is just clay-eating crackers who made their money out of colored folks.

"Why, I remember that Beauregard Jones' pappy trying to chase me through a cotton field one time. And I sure give him a piece of my mind. I didn't fool around with no trashy peckerwoods."

But Mrs. Ida Baker was right. Mrs. Dr. Cassett *did* give a big tea that next Saturday and she *didn't* invite Mrs. Evangeline.

And the very next Friday, Mrs. Evangeline gave a catered dinner at her summer home out on Little River (although it was only April) and she not only didn't invite Mrs. Dr. Cassett; she also didn't invite any of Mrs. Dr. Cassett's kinfolks.

Mrs. Dr. Cassett came right back the next week and gave a barbecue out at the Hopkinsville Country Club and not only didn't invite Mrs. Evangeline and her relatives; she also omitted some of Mrs. Evangeline's best friends.

From then on, the war was out in the open, and everybody was a bit upset. Everybody, that is, except my Uncle John Braxton, the Barbecue Poet Laureate of the State of Kentucky, and Mrs. Rebecca Williams, our leading colored caterer.

Both of them found themselves with so much work to do that they almost had to slight some older customers. Uncle John, who never got mixed up in white folks' business, hardly knew what was going on.

But Mrs. Rebecca was quite aware of what was happening, and there were reports that she was helping to keep the feud alive.

Mrs. Ida Baker, who resented the fact that Mrs. Dr. Cassett had called in an outside caterer to run her parties, told Grandma Hettie that Mrs. Rebecca was taking tales from one party to the other and telling each what the other was supposed to have said about her on the last occasion.

And Mrs. Rosa Coldweather and Mrs. Cecelia Coole were busy

imitating their quality white folks in our colored community. First, Mrs. Rosa gave a musicale at the Elks Home and didn't invite Mrs. Cecelia. And Mrs. Cecelia came right back by not inviting Mrs. Rosa to her Paul Laurence Dunbar Poetry Circle reading the next week.

Papa, who was Dean of Men at Kentucky State Normal College for Negroes and who only got home from Frankfort, Ky., every other week, was very amused by the feuding. But Mama wasn't amused at all.

"It's got to the point that you don't know what to do," Mama said; "If you don't invite both of them to a social, they think you're taking sides. And if one finds out the other's been invited, then neither one of them will come."

And Papa would just laugh and poke fun at both of them.

But Papa stopped laughing when Judge Hezekiah Witherspoon, our town's Republican leader, called him down to the courthouse to face the situation. Papa discussed the matter with Mama when he came back home that night.

"Eph," Judge Witherspoon had said, "You know that I don't mix with social things in our colored community. But when you all start trouble among our quality families, then somebody's got to put a halt to it."

Papa pretended he didn't know what Judge Witherspoon was talking about, but the judge wouldn't let him get away with it.

"Now, Eph," he said, "you're an ungrateful Democrat but you know what's going on in this town. And Jim Williams (our colored courthouse janitor) tells me the whole thing started out there in the Booker T. Washington Colored Grammar School.

"He tells me that that Rosa Coldweather and Cecelia Coole got mad with each other and then stirred up Mrs. Dr. Cassett and Mrs. Evangeline Jones against each other.

"Now this thing's got so bad that Dr. Cassett and Mr. Beauregard Jones ain't speaking to each other neither. And both of them is going into debt paying for all these foolish frolics their womenfolks are pulling off every week.

"Well, we Republicans are having enough trouble keeping Christian County without having our two biggest committeemen not speaking to each other.

"This may make you happy as a Democrat, but I don't think you want nothing to happen to that Rosa or Cecelia. And if this foolishness doesn't stop soon, something's going to happen to somebody. I can tell you that."

Papa pretended to think the matter over deliberately, as he always did in his conferences with Judge Witherspoon. And then he offered a possible solution.

"I don't think you need to do anything drastic, Judge," he told him. "As a matter of fact, you might end this whole thing with a gesture which might do you some good."

The Judge leaned forward anxiously as Papa explained.

"The Male and Female College for Colored here has an elementary school department," Papa said, "and if the Republicans should offer a full paid scholarship there for a deserving Negro student, it might ease everything. The tuition would only be $35 a year."

The Judge was a little reluctant, but Papa, as usual, finally sold him on the idea.

And that is why Mrs. Oceola Watkins came rushing breathlessly to our house the next morning to tell Mama that her bright son, Oswald, had just won an unusual honor.

"He was so much smarter than the other boys," she said, "that they done give him a scholarship at the Male and Female College for Colored so he won't be held back in his classes."

Mama congratulated her warmly and frowned severely at Grandma Hettie when she took her corn cob pipe out of her mouth. So Grandma Hettie just put her pipe back and didn't say anything.

Rat Joiner, Tack-Haired Baker and a few of the other guys who didn't know what was going on were a little jealous of Knee Baby's good fortune at first. Especially since Knee Baby went around bragging that he was going to be a college man in the fourth grade.

"I can learn heap much more better up there," he boasted.

I don't know how much Papa's scheme really accomplished. But it was a fact that three months after Knee Baby left the Booker T.

Washington Colored Grammar School, Mrs. Rosa and Mrs. Cecelia started talking to each other again. And it wasn't too long after that that Mrs. Evangeline invited Mrs. Dr. Cassett to her July 4th picnic.

Everybody was happy about it except Mrs. Rebecca Williams, whose catering business was suddenly shot to pieces.

But none of us young tads were surprised the next year when the Male and Female College for Colored suddenly shut down after a fist fight between the President and the Dean of Men.

We'd expected something like that from the moment that Knee Baby Watkins joined the student body.

COUSIN BLIND MARY

I had never paid the matter much mind myself, for I had just assumed that we Postons were pretty well-off colored people in Hopkinsville—what with Papa being Dean of Men at the Kentucky State Industrial College for Negroes, and Mama still Director of Domestic Science for Colored for the whole state of Kentucky.

So I was a bit surprised one day at the Booker T. Washington Colored Grammar School to hear Rat Joiner refer to us as "poor relations of Miss Blind Mary." Rat must have sensed my surprise because he stopped talking to Tack-Haired Baker and turned to me.

"Yeah, Ted," he said, "I know you Postons got a couple of nickels to rub against a dime. But Miss Blind Mary's got money's mammy. Few *white* folks and no Negroes at *all* got more money than Miss Blind Mary, that high yaller, fortune-telling cousin of you alls."[1]

And, come to think of it, there was an element of truth—as usual—in what Rat said.

For although our six-room house out on Hayes Street (with the first inside toilet in the whole community) was comfortable enough for me and Mama and Papa, and my ten brothers and sisters, it could hardly be compared with the cute little bungalow Cousin Blind Mary had built up on Belmont Hill, pretty close to the quality white folks' houses.

And our house would have been even more comfortable if Papa hadn't decided sometime during my second year in the Booker T. Washington Colored Grammar School that all of our girl cousins—

31

the Braxtons, the Coxes and all of them—should have the benefit of an education too.

So as soon as every one of them finished the Christian County Academy for Colored, they'd wind up living in our house while they went to our Crispus Attucks Negro High School—before Papa got them into the Kentucky State Industrial College for Negroes up in Frankfort.

No one was happier than me to see each one of them graduate from Attucks and head for Frankfort. For not only did all of my girl cousins make themselves at home on Hayes Street; they also felt they had to take a hand in my upbringing. So they were all more than anxious to bop me over the head on any and all occasions.

My cousin Arabella Braxton went even further. She watched my Grandma Hettie Cox and adopted one of Grandma's favorite tactics. She would bop me over the head regularly and say: "That's for nothing; now watch out."

But it wasn't their fault that Rat Joiner could refer to us as "poor relations of Miss Blind Mary." That was Papa's fault alone.

Of course, neither Papa nor Mama ever told me how much money they made in their two big jobs. I was perfectly willing to settle for the crates of watermelon pickles, sweet potato pies, canned dandelion greens and pickled pigs' feet that Mama brought home on her periodic swings around the state as Director of Domestic Science for Colored.

And surely none of my innumerable girl cousins contributed to any financial shorts we might have encountered. All of them were too well brought up as good country girls to come back from a visit to their farm without bringing a courtesy gift—like a sugar-cured ham, a smoked shoulder, a sack of pork sausage, or a bushel of corn or sweet potatoes—in season, of course.

In fact, Mama had so much stuff packed in our smokehouse down beside the stable that Grandma Hettie almost deserted her religious upbringing once for pure larceny.

"You know, Arabella," I once heard her tell Mrs. Arabella Jones, her longtime childhood intimate from the old Reconstruction Days

32

on the Peay Plantation down near Clarksville, Tennessee. "I just got an idea that will keep us both in snuff as long as we live.

"My Mollie's got more produce stuffed away in that smokehouse than she and Eph and all them children will ever be able to use up in a year. Now, you got a shed out there in back of your house across the street.

"So one of these days while Mollie is traipsing all over with that domestic science foolishness, and Eph's up there in Frankfort, why don't we stash out half of that stuff in your back-yard shack? And I'll buy a new lock and key.

"And then some of these times when we come up short and can't afford a little Bull Durham pipe tobacco, or a good chew or some snuff, all we have to do is call some friends who ain't big-mouth and sell them what they want. Shucks, one of them fifteen-pound sugar-cured hams would be sure to bring a dollar, if not a doll 'n' a half. And we could smoke, chew or sniff a whole month on one ham alone!"

And Grandma Hettie almost got away with it. Except that Mrs. Arabella had just been elected Second Deaconess of the Virginia Street Baptist Church—and already had her eye on the First Deaconess spot.

"Why Hettie," she said to Grandma Hettie Cox, "some people would call that *dishonest*. And can't you see what that Nixola Green (the First Deaconess) would make out of it when she finds out I'm going to run against her in next August's election?"

Of course, Mrs. Arabella changed her mind after Mrs. Nixola Green beat her out in the August race at the Virginia Street Baptist Church. But Grandma had also changed her mind.

"Naw, Arabella," I heard her say the next time the subject came up (both of them, as usual, ignoring my presence under the piano in the parlor that rainy day). "I just couldn't do it. The Devil must have thunk the whole thing up before I mentioned it. But I just couldn't be taking food out of them poor children's mouths. Especially since that Eph my Mollie married is determined to send us all to the poor house."

Mrs. Arabella seemed as mystified as I was. So I stopped cutting the tassel off my sister Lillian's knitted stocking cap (which I planned to pin on my shoulder and play like I was a kindly Confederate General) and listened as Grandma Hettie explained.

"That Eph," she went on, "he ain't content to be the first Negro with a sheepskin in this county. That educated fool ain't content to be the one man to settle all the bets of the sporting men and the 'bounds' of the deacons and the elders. Naw, he's decided he's got to be a business man. And him not able to count beyond two and two makes four."

(Now I was a Papa man myself in any dispute with Grandma Hettie. But I had to admit that she had something there. I had already decided that Papa was a little weak in arithmetic.

(He had always been willing—if not anxious—to help me with my homework. He had even encouraged me to challenge Miss Annabelle Breckinridge, my Fourth Grade teacher, when she insisted that pure and kindly General Robert E. Lee was a better soldier than that old likker-head Ulysses Simpson Grant. "Ask her who won," he'd suggest, to the open disapproval of Mama, who believed in strict classroom decorum for young tads.

(But when we got around to arithmetic, Papa always seemed busy. "Ask your Mama about that," he'd always say. And Mama would take over with a barely-masked gleam of triumph. I might add: it didn't help. I *was* Papa's son.

(But I figured all this out later. I was still listening to Grandma Hettie and Mrs. Arabella from under the piano.)

"That Eph!" she was saying. "Naw, he ain't content to be taking more money from them white folks up there in Frankfort than he's got any right to expect. He's got to show that he's got as much sense as real high yaller business men, like Undertaker Mr. Ed Smith and Mr. Rich Redd who's got his own store his white folks give him up there on Younglove Street."

Mrs. Arabella took another dip of snuff and waited. Along with me.

"So he sent up there to Chicago or somewhere, and got him this measuring book from Sears Roebuck or somebody. And now he's in the measured-clothes business.[2]

"I heard him tell my Mollie that them suits cost fifteen dollars a piece, and that he gets three dollars in front from each suit. So as soon as he practices up on his measurements, he's gonna set up in business and make more money than any Mose mogul in this area."

Well, this explained one thing. I had been mystified how Papa seemed to be appearing suddenly out of unexpected places every time B'Rob (my brother, Robert Abraham Lincoln) or General (my brother Ulysses Simpson Grant) showed up in any hallway. He seemed to be grabbing them, making them crook an elbow, and drawing this measuring cord on them. Once or twice he threw a speculative glance in my direction, but I guess the Chicago company wasn't in business for little tads then.

But pretty soon, although it was vacation time, Papa disappeared from the scene. He didn't even come back for the fortnightly meetings where he settled all bets between the betting men and the bounding men. But he was apparently doing a pretty good business in Hopkinsville, too.

Rat summed up the local situation:

"They got to order them store-bought suits from him," Rat concluded, "cause if they don't, they'll think he might rule against them when they bring some bet to him to be settled."

And I figured Papa was doing all right, because I heard him tell Mama one night:

"Mollie, I'm doing all right. I made thirty-three dollars here in Hopkinsville today alone—eleven suits. And I didn't even ask most of them. And you should know how well I'm doing all over the state."

Mama didn't say nothing back. But this wasn't surprising. She had known Papa much longer than I had. Not that I wasn't still a Papa man.

But the bubble burst three weeks later. Mr. Smoky Smith, our sporting man, dropped by to see Papa.

Now everybody in Hopkinsville knew Smoky Smith's uniform—

a pair of tailor-made trousers and a blue overall jumper faded light by the three washings Smoky insisted it went through before he wore it the first time.

But this time—in the middle of the week—the jumper hadn't been washed even once. But even more important, Mr. Smoky Smith's tailor-made pants (which he had always bought with a whole suit since Sears and Roebuck or somebody didn't believe in job lots) wasn't quite right.

One leg was about eight inches shorter than the other.

Smoky didn't say anything. He just walked up the front steps and looked at Papa—while Papa looked at that left leg.

Without a word, Papa reached in his pocket and handed Smoky his fifteen dollars.

And before any other customers could arrive—and, oh boy, they did arrive with the next mail—Papa went down to talk the matter over with Mr. Beauregard Jones, President of the First Tobacco and Planters Trust Company.

And we got something called a "mortgage" on our Hayes Street home.

I never got around to asking Papa what a "mortgage" was, because he went right out across the state giving people back what they had paid him for them tailor-made clothes. But I gathered from Mama's attitude that a mortgage was nothing good.

"Professor Poston," I heard her say to him one night, "Nobody makes money on his bottom but a shoemaker. So, why don't you stick to your last and keep teaching them young-uns up in Frankfort how to mind their manners without no tailor-made suits. Not that any of them—thank God—was able to afford your measurements."

And the whole matter might have ended there had not Mrs. Ida James chosen to stick her two cents in. Mrs. Ida had grown up with Mama and Cousin Blind Mary and—since Cousin Blind Mary built that little house up on Belmont Hill—had been calling herself Cousin Blind Mary's "companion."

"Companion nothing," I had heard Mama say once. "That Mary works her harder than any white folks ever would. And pays her less than she could get at the poor house."

But Mrs. Ida didn't see it that way. Especially since Cousin Blind Mary had moved out among the white folks, and had only a few colored old-timers as customers.

So she came in to console Mama on Papa's business venture.

"If he had just asked Miss Blind Mary in front," she told Mama, ignoring a patting foot I had learned early to mind, "Professor Poston wouldn't be in this state all over the state. Why, Miss Blind Mary would have told him this make-to-measure business was not for him."

Mama, who was never sharp with anybody, only said: "Ida, why don't you mind you and Mary's and the white folks' business and leave me and Professor Poston alone?"

And Mrs. Ida shot back: "I'm telling you this free. If you had asked Miss Blind Mary it would have cost you plenty."

"Ida James," said Mama, her left foot picking up acceleration, "Don't tell me nothing about that Mary Cox . . ."

But Mrs. Ida James cut back in.

"I know what you thinking about—when we was young," she said, "but Miss Blind Mary's got the gift. Why, just last week she straightened things out for Judge Hezekiah Witherspoon and that little niece of his who got into trouble. . . ."

Well, I sat right still under the dining room table where I was cutting out pictures from the *Ladies Home Journal* which I had planned to send anonymously to little Sarah Williams. Because this business of Judge Hezekiah Witherspoon's niece being "in trouble" interested me.

For my part, I just couldn't imagine white folks being in trouble. They were *white* weren't they?

And I hadn't been particularly enlightened one day downtown when Rat Joiner and I had seen little Viola Witherspoon almost run over by the fire wagon which was rushing to put out a blaze in the white folks' neighborhood.

"She don't seem to know that she can be knocked *down,* too," Rat had said.

Mama said to Mrs. Ida, "What do you mean, she straightened out Judge Hezekiah Witherspoon?"

"Well," said Mrs. Ida James, "the Judge knew she had been going to dances and things out at the country club with that little Jim Meadows fellow whose folks ain't got no more stuff than a hog's got feathers. So, since that little Viola refused to say nothing, the Judge thought he was the one. So he come over to talk the matter over with Miss Blind Mary.

"And Miss Blind Mary asked him to give her a day to mull it over in her glass ball, and said that the next day she would let him know who it was.

"And sure enough, next day she told him that it wasn't that little Jim Meadows fellow at all; it was the first grandson of Mr. Beauregard Jones, the President of the First Tobacco and Planters Trust Company, who had been messing around with Miss Viola.

"And the Judge went right to that little Jeff Davis Beauregard and he admitted it right away. And everybody was happy. Especially Miss Blind Mary who got quite a nice gift from Judge Hezekiah Witherspoon."

I guess my Uncle John Braxton was pretty happy about the whole thing too. As Barbecue Poet Laureate of Kentucky, he catered the affair, and charged them so much a head at the wedding reception.

But that wasn't Cousin Blind Mary's biggest coup since she moved up there among the white folks.

There had been that big time when Mr. Beauregard Jones had decided to check the accounts before he went on his annual vacation trip cat-fishing. And his routine check showed that somebody had come up short some fifty-thousand dollars.

Mr. Beauregard Jones was quite upset about it. Maybe fifty thousand dollars isn't much money where some banks are concerned, but it was a lot of money where the First Tobacco and Planters' Trust Company was concerned. So Mr. Beauregard kept the news from his white folks (naturally we Negroes knew all about it) except for his son-in-law, Mr. Edward Greer, who seemed just as mystified as he was.

So it was only natural that Mr. Beauregard Jones should take his problem to Cousin Blind Mary. And Cousin Blind Mary, as usual, asked for twenty-four hours in which to study the problem through her glass dome.

And when Mr. Beauregard Jones came back the next night, (according to Mrs. Ida James) Cousin Blind Mary was ready for him.

"The crystal ball wasn't altogether clear," she told Mr. Beauregard Jones, "but it told me that if you will go up to the L. & N. Station tomorrow night to meet the Dixie Express, you'll find the man who's got your money boarding that train and trying to get down to Nashville."

Well, Mr. Beauregard Jones went up to the L. & N. Station and met the Dixie Express at 9:15 P.M. And who was getting on that train for Nashville? Nobody but his ever-loving son-in-law, Mr. Edward Greer.

Most of the white folks never heard about it, and all of us kept quiet. So Mr. Beauregard Jones just kept the thirty-seven thousand five hundred he found in Mr. Edward Greer's suitcase, and made up the difference himself. And Mr. Edward Greer finally left town unhampered after Mr. Beauregard Jones' horse-faced daughter sued him for divorce.

But from that moment, Cousin Blind Mary had it made.

So, all of us were a bit surprised a few months later when Cousin Blind Mary gave up the fortune-telling business and announced that she was leaving Hopkinsville, Kentucky, for good.

And she did, too.

But she made one mistake. She should have taken Mrs. Ida James—or paid her hush-mouth money.

For as soon as Cousin Blind Mary left town—without paying her "companion" off—Mrs. Ida James put her business in the streets.

"Mollie," I heard Mrs. James tell Mama one night. "You know she wasn't no fortune-teller. And you know why she had to give it up."

Mama just nodded in agreement, but Papa asked the question I would have asked if little tads had been permitted to join in old folks' conversations.

"But why did she quit?" Papa asked.

"Because Aunt Fanny died, and Miss Susie moved up to Indianapolis with them grandchildren of hers, and Miss Eddie just got too old to work anymore—"

But me and Papa were still mystified. So Papa asked: "Well, what's that got to do with it?"

And Mama exploded in exasperation.

"You men," she said, "you're as dumb as white folks. Don't tell me, Professor Poston, that you thought Blind Mary was really getting those things out of that crystal ball. Why do you think she always asked for a night to consult the spirits?"

"Well, she needed that night to talk to Aunt Fanny, Miss Susie, Miss Eddie or whoever else was working for the white folks involved. That's how she found out that Mr. Edward Greer had been tapping the till in Mr. Beauregard Jones' bank for years, and that he planned to make his getaway on the Dixie Express that night.

"So when the old folks started dying out, quitting and moving out of town, that Blind Mary knew that the jig (if you'll pardon the expression) was up. So she got out while the getting was good."

And then Mama dropped a real bomb shell.

"And while we are on the subject," she said, "That Blind Mary is no cousin of mine. Mama Hettie just sort of adopted her so we could have at least one high-yaller in the family.

"And I don't think she was blind either. I remember when we used to play Blind Man's Buff when we all were little tads. Of course we didn't put a blindfold on Mary when she was 'it.' And she always managed to find the one who had done something nasty to her. And she'd bop them, but good."

5

PAPA WAS A DEMOCRAT

Papa was the only Negro Democrat in our Hopkinsville, Ky., or in the whole state of Kentucky for that matter.[1] And this made it very difficult for me in my first years at the Booker T. Washington Colored Grammar School.

For while Rat Joiner, Tack-Haired Baker and the rest of my friends had only to put up with "playing the dozens" (that is, having your opponents say nasty things about your mother), my enemies always ended all arguments with me by yelling:

"Your Pappy's a Democrat."

At first, I didn't know exactly what a Democrat was, but I gathered it was regarded as something dirty in our colored community. So I was always forced to carry the argument one step further by busting my opponent in the nose.

But there was no fence built around my nose either, so I didn't always win the argument by this stratagem.

I didn't take the matter up immediately with Papa, though, even after my first half dozen bloody noses. I guess I was sort of afraid he might answer "Yes" if I put the question to him directly. And then where would I be?

But the real reason was that Papa was a busy man—being Professor Ephraim Poston, Dean of Men at the Kentucky State Industrial

College for Negroes at Frankfort, Ky.—and he only got home every other week-end.

And on those rare occasions when he arrived, he didn't have too much time for me, the last of his 11 children. And very little time for the other 10 either.

For, as the first Negro college graduate in Hopkinsville, Ky.— he'd finished Walden College down in Nashville long before the turn of the century—he believed in fulfilling his community responsibilities.

And one of these responsibilities was to settle all the arguments and bets on any constituted dispute of facts which had arisen during his absence in Frankfort.

In fact, the only way we children knew for sure sometimes that Papa was due in town on Saturdays was when our front porch started filling up early in the morning with disputants on both sides.

All the sporting men would stand on the left-hand side of the steps, putting their bets into neutral hands and waiting for Papa to render his immutable decisions.

The seekers after truth and the more respectable disputants would range themselves comfortably in the swing and benches on the porch itself and ignore the riff-raff down the steps.

Papa would finally arrive, put his carpet bag in the living room, and then stroll out to meet his callers.

The routine never varied. First there were the usual amenities. Who had been feeling poorly? How were things with the Elks?

(I remember Papa asked the latter question once of Mr. Ezekial Quarles, our long-time Imperial Potentate. And when Mr. Quarles replied, "Well, 'Fesser Poston, the Elks ain't doing so well right now. . . ." Papa consoled him as quick as a flash with: "Gee, I'm sorry to hear it, Zeke. I didn't know you lost the last election. Who is Imperial Potentate now?")

But after the amenities were over, the elders would get in their questions.

The opening gambit was always reserved for Mr. Freddie Williams, who had been First Deacon of the Virginia Street Baptist Church ever since we bought the structure from the white folks.

"Well, Professor Poston," he would start, "Just how do you spell this 'Nebbie-ker-neezer'?"

And Papa would say, "N-e-b-u-c-h-a-d-n-e-z-z-a-r."

"Now ain't that something?" Mr. Williams would ask, sneaking a look at the piece of paper he had in his hand. And if he had it written down right, he'd smirk at Mr. Ronald Childress, the first elder of the Dirt's Ave. African Methodist Episcopal Church.[2]

(Being men of religion, the deacons and elders never made a *bet*. But they challenged each other by saying "I'll *bound* you a million that such-and-such ain't so.")

Then Mr. J. B. Petty, our local insurance man who fancied himself as Hopkinsville's best Negro historian, would show off his erudition by asking:

"Now, Professor Poston, what was the name of that proud African tribe who boasted that they all remained jet black even in slavery, and that no white folks' blood had ever coursed through their veins?"

And Papa would hesitate thoughtfully before answering. And then he would say:

"Well, J.B., I don't think it was any *particular* African tribe that made the boast. It was just a number of individual slaves from various tribes who boasted that their blood lines were pure.

"As a matter of fact, they often called themselves 'Salt Water Negroes,' meaning that their racial strain was as undiluted then as it was the day their forebears were brought in shackles over the ocean."

And while everybody stood aghast at Papa's knowledge, he would break the spell by saying:

"But, J.B., I don't think you have to worry about that. You took good pains to see that none of your children would be salt water Negroes."

And both front porch and lawn would break out in raucous laughter. For although his intimates sometimes joked Mr. J. B.

Petty that he was so dark at birth that his mother didn't find him for five months, everybody knew that he was inordinately proud of his marriage to Miss Aurelia Scott. For few white folks and no Negroes at all were lighter than Miss Aurelia in Hopkinsville, Ky. But soon the historians and theologians would be disposed of, and the sporting men would get down to business.

Smoky Smith, who wore his black Stetson hat without a dent anywhere in the crown, and a starched blue denim jumper over his black serge tailor-made pants, was always the first in this category. Nobody ever dared challenge his precedence.

"Now, Mr. Eph," Smoky would say, "What were the odds on the Jack Johnson–Jeff Willard fight?" and then facetiously, "Who won?"

And although Papa was not a betting man himself, he'd say:

"The odds, as I recall them, were 8 to 5 on Willard. And I seem to remember that Johnson won."

The laughter had hardly subsided after Smoky collected his bet when somebody like Set-the-Meat Jones would ask:

"And how many years did George Dixon fight before he hung up his gloves?"

And Papa would come back with: "Just about 21 years, Edward." (Papa never used the more descriptive nicknames.) "I think he fought his first fight in 1886 and hung up his gloves for good in 1906—the same year little Ted here was born."

And then the questions would go on to Joe Gans, Sam Langford, the original Joe Walcott and other of our pugilists of note. I can never remember a question about a white fighter in all these sessions, or about a bout where a Negro got licked.

Neither can I ever remember anybody checking back on Papa. If Professor said it was so, it was so. Papa did have a prodigious memory and if anybody ever caught him wrong, they didn't have nerve enough to tell him so.

So it was understandable that I waited six weeks—and eight bloody noses—before I screwed up my courage enough to raise the question which had been racking my brain (not to mention rocking my head in daily combat) at the Booker T. Washington Colored Grammar School.

And I probably wouldn't have had nerve enough to ask it even then if I hadn't been forced to take on a double-header the day before in the Booker T. playground.

It had started out as a simple fight between me and Copper-Mouth Papa Peterson. Only he wasn't called Copper-Mouth then, but just plain Oscar. It was only in later years when he became a sporting man that he got the nickname Copper-Mouth Papa.

Allison Williams gave it to him that day Oscar came back from Louisville where, as a sporting man, he had had extensive dental work done. But he was nicknamed for life when Allison cried:

"Look at that doggone Oscar. He's got a mouth full of gold teeth. And ain't no two of them the same color. They got to be *copper.*"

I don't remember exactly what the original argument was between me and Oscar that day at Booker T. Washington Colored Grammar School. But when he could think of nothing else to say, he yelled at me in scorn:

"And anyway, your Pappy's a Democrat!"

And I let him have it right where the gold teeth were later to appear.[3]

It wasn't my first set-to with Oscar. And I had no doubt that I could take him again. And I would have too if Leonardius Wright hadn't chosen that minute to put his two cents worth in.

Leonardius was my rival for the affections of pretty little Sarah Williams, and he'd had it in for me ever since he learned I was writing her love letters too in our Third Grade Class. So when me and Oscar locked horns in the playground, Leonardius started cheering Oscar on.

"Let him have it, Oscar," he was yelling from the sidelines, "Give him a *white* eye."

Now Leonardius knew that was wrong, and that he had deliberately broken an unwritten convention. Nobody as high yaller as Leonardius was supposed to raise the complexion question with nobody as dark as me—although Mama always insisted I was a pretty chocolate brown.

Anyway, I turned to glare at Leonardius out of my right eye and Oscar landed a haymaker in my left before I could turn back again.

So I forfeited the fight to Oscar on a matter of higher principle, and caught up with Leonardius just before he scampered through the back door of the Booker T. Washington Colored Grammar School.

And then I proceeded to give him two *black* eyes as a lesson for the future.

Therefore, early the next morning when the signifiers started gathering on our front porch to await Papa's fortnightly arrival, I hurried down to the L. & N. railroad station so I could stroll back home with him and have a few minutes alone.

And as we walked away from the station—where Papa had spent a few minutes settling a couple of bets between Mr. Sam Owens, the baggage clerk, and Mr. Edward Wynn, our colored porter—I took the bull by the horns.

"Papa," I said without preamble, as we approached Ninth and Campbell Streets, "Are you a Democrat?"

He considered the question with his usual deliberation and then said:

"Why no, son. I'm neither a Democrat nor a Republican. I just vote for men and measures. Party labels mean nothing to me."

I mulled this over for another block—in both hope and despair—and ventured another query:

"But, Papa, didn't you ever vote for the Republicans some time?"

"Come to think of it," he rejoined, "I don't think I ever did. They never nominated a Republican around here that I thought was worth voting for."

I mulled over that until we got to Second and Vine Streets, only three blocks from home. And then I ventured:

"Miss Hazel Green, our Third Grade teacher, says our colored citizens shouldn't vote for the Democrats. She said it ain't fair to Mr. Abraham Lincoln."[4]

Papa chuckled to himself as we walked over the little bridge at Gulley Street. But finally he said:

"Son, I never voted against Mr. Lincoln. He hasn't been on the ballot for years and years as far as I know. Matter of fact, I was a little tyke just about your age when John Wilkes Booth shot Mr. Lincoln dead."

"Dead?" I echoed automatically. And then I shut up. I knew that my history book in the Booker T. Washington Colored Grammar School said something about Mr. Lincoln being shot, but you would never have guessed that he was dead—from the way our leading politicians and teachers talked about him.

But we were home by that time and I was carrying Papa's carpet bag into the living room as Mr. Freddie Williams was preparing to ask the day's first question.

I never raised the question again with Papa, but I found out later that it was not by any means a dead issue in his mind.

On his next trip home, for instance, he brought me a new history book he'd ordered from way up North—as far up there as Cleveland or some such place. And it taught me a lot of things I'd never learned in Booker T. Washington Colored Grammar School.

I started to wonder, for one thing, if Mr. Robert E. Lee was *really* a better general than old Ulysses Simpson Grant (for whom one of my brothers was named).

I also began to have my doubts about Mr. Stonewall Jackson and to question for the first time whether that blood-thirsty old rascal, General Sherman, actually ate pure and innocent little white babies for breakfast every morning as he made his march through Georgia.

But Papa wasn't content just doing this to *me*. He carried the whole matter further. He started pushing his twice-monthly front porch seminars far beyond the usual questions and answers, and began talking to our visitors about "men and measures" and local politics.

Oddly enough, it was the sporting men down on the front lawn who first started listening. They didn't care who was Mayor or City Clerk or Circuit Judge.

But they were a little fed up with Mr. Sidney Lanier Jenkins, our Republican sheriff in Christian County. It seemed that in recent weeks, Mr. Jenkins—or his collectors—had doubled the ante the sporting men had to pay for running an innocent little poker or pitty-pat game, or for selling a little "mountain dew" corn liquor, or even for just keeping out of jail.

But nobody seemed to pay Papa no real mind until the returns were counted in that next April's elections. And, come and behold, the whole Republican ticket was elected—with the sole exception of Mr. Jenkins. And when they counted up the votes out on Dirt's Avenue and Lovier's Hill where most of the sporting people lived, they found out that 113 colored citizens had voted Democratic for the first time, while Sheriff Jenkins had lost the county-wide race by only 103 votes.

Papa was pretty put up by the whole thing. But Mama didn't seem too happy. For while Papa was back up in Frankfort the next week, she heard the rumors that were going around the town.

It seemed that Cock-Eye Watson and Ozie Jones, the two colored citizens who used to collect his graft for Sheriff Jenkins, felt that Papa had done them a personal disservice in getting their boss defeated. And they boasted they weren't going to take it lying down.

In fact, every time they got high in Pete Postell's saloon—where drinks for them were no longer on the house—they boasted that they were going to shoot that Eph Poston dead the next time they saw him.

Papa didn't pay them no mind in spite of Mama's apprehensions. But the reports got so widespread that Judge Hezekiah Witherspoon, our local Republican leader, heard about them. And he sent word to Mama to have Papa come straight to his office the next time he came home.

Papa did and Judge Witherspoon came right to the point.

"Eph," he said, Papa told us later, "You are a Democrat—God

knows why—and you've never done us no good. But you are also one of our leading colored citizens. And we are not going to have our good colored citizens bothered by no riff-raff."

Then he reached in his roll-top desk and handed Papa two big horse pistols.

"You take these guns and go right out there and shoot those two Nigras dead. And I'll see that nobody does a thing about it."

Papa had never owned a pistol in his life, but he was too polite to offend Judge Witherspoon. So he picked up the guns with mixed emotions. For one thing, he knew that Judge Witherspoon hadn't been too unhappy about the defeat of Sheriff Jenkins. For Mr. Jim Williams, our courthouse janitor, had told him the Judge had long been dissatisfied with the way Sheriff Jenkins was splitting his "take."

For another, Papa knew he wasn't going to shoot anybody.

But I didn't learn the sequel until late the next afternoon when I was digging fishing worms under the back porch and Mama and Papa were sitting up there in the shade talking things over.

"I've never felt so silly in my life," Papa was telling Mama. "There I was walking down Sixth Street with two big horse pistols in my pockets. And I knew I'd never bring them home.

"So as I was passing Pete Postell's Saloon, I got an idea. I'd give the pistols to Pete and he could dispose of them as he saw fit.

"But when I walked in the bar with those two big pistols in my hands, the first two people I saw were Cock-Eye Watson and Ozie Jones.

"We all saw each other at the same time. But they took one look at those big horse pistols and almost broke each other's necks in scrambling out the back door family entrance. They actually tore one side off the swinging doors."

Mama chuckled quietly, but by the next day the story was all over town. One wag swore on his oath that:

"Ozie and Cock-Eye didn't stop running until they got to the L. & N. Station. And then they took the first thing out of there smoking. It turned out to be a Pullman conductor with a pipe in his mouth. But they rode him as far as Evansville, Indiana, before they found out their mistake."

I always doubted that Papa's detractors left town that fast. But nobody ever saw them around anymore after that night.

And anyway, the incident solved my own personal problem.

For nobody else for the rest of our school term dared insult the son of Two-Gun Eph Poston—even if his father *was* a Democrat.[5]

6

MR. BEEFER JONES

I first met Mr. Beefer Jones through his two little tad nephews, Sam Brown and James Wilkes, both Fourth Grade classmates of mine at the Booker T. Washington Colored Grammar School in Hopkinsville, Kentucky.[1] And Grandma Hettie had been a little miffed when she learned that I had gone home with Sam and James one day, to the pretty little bungalow where they lived with Mr. Beefer Jones and his Chicago-born wife, Aunt Beth, over on Fourth Street.

"That Orlando Jones ain't nothing but a gambling man," Grandma Hettie complained to Mama. "I don't know why the white folks let him run that poker and pitty-pat game over the livery stable down there on Ninth Street."[2]

Papa, who happened to be home that week-end from his job as Dean of Men at the Kentucky State Industrial College for Negroes up in Frankfort, ventured a guess.

"Well, one reason the white folks might not bother Orlando," he said, "is that I hear he pays Mr. Sidney Lanier Jenkins, our Republican sheriff, twenty-five dollars each and every week for the privilege. And I do hear that Orlando's giving both his little nephews everything they need. So he must have a little bit left after he gives Sheriff Jenkins his weekly cut."

Now, Grandma Hettie always admired success, so she sort of back-tracked by observing:

"They do say he'll bet on anything—that fire won't burn, that butter beans ain't fat, or that lard ain't greasy."

(Which showed how much she knew about it—if Mr. Smoky

Smith, our *real* gambling man, was to be believed. And nobody ever kept a mouthful of teeth—gold *or* ivory—if they questioned Mr. Smoky Smith's word.

(I'd heard Mr. Smoky Smith tell Mr. Hezekiah Williams, while they were waiting on our front lawn for Papa to come home and settle some factual bets which came up when he was up in Frankfort:

("That bugaboo, Beefer Jones, ain't never bet cash on nothing—not even that the sun would rise the next morning. He makes his by just cutting them games he runs up at the Pleasure Emporium—ten cents from the winner of each pitty-pat hand; twenty-five cents on each poker hand. But he gets his *real* money from the five cents he charges on each pass of the dice.")

But what had me worried was that both Papa and Grandma Hettie had referred to Mr. Beefer as "Orlando." Then why did everyone else call him "Beefer"?

I raised the question at their house one day after Sunday School. I went there every Sunday if Mama went to the 1 P.M. communion service at the Virginia Street Baptist Church, because I knew Aunt Beth subscribed to a Chicago paper called *The Tribune*. This paper had some pretty good murder stories. (Papa had me reading long before I ever entered the Booker T. Washington Colored Grammar School. I don't remember when I picked up the habit, but I was a sucker for a whodunit.)

So that Sunday I asked Sam about his uncle's two names.

"If your uncle, Mr. Beefer Jones, is named 'Orlando'—as Grandma Hettie and Papa called him the other day, then why does everybody else call him 'Beefer'?"

Sam glanced out the front window and said:

"He had a big game of show-down poker in the place last night and all through this morning, and he's just coming up the front steps right now. You just listen to him for about five minutes, and you'll know why they call him 'Beefer.'"

Mr. Beefer Jones came in, loosening his tie and pulling off his shirt before he was hardly in the front door.

"Drag that tub in the kitchen and make it as hot as I can stand it, Beth," he was saying to Aunt Beth. "We really *had* one at the place last night, and I feel I can soak for a week."

(Sam, who had his own ideas about his uncle, Mr. Beefer Jones, was to tell me later: "He's really an ankle and elbow man. And that's as far as I've seen him go in a tub in all the years I've been here. But whenever he comes in with company in the house, he always asks Aunt Beth for a full tub."

(Rat Joiner insisted later that he was just putting on a show for Professor Ephraim Poston's littlest son. For, because Papa's rulings were the last word on all non-gambling wagers among Hopkinsville's bettors and bounders, Papa was a celebrity in Mr. Beefer Jones' gambling house.)

Mr. Beefer Jones had spotted me the minute he came into the parlor, but he made a big thing of finding me there—with a copy of the *Chicago Tribune* on my knee.

"What are you reading, boy?" he asked, strolling over to pull last week's paper off my knee. "Oh, that Loeb-Leopold thing."

And then I got my first indication of where Mr. Beefer Jones got his name. He looked at the paper and remarked:

"I read that piece last Wednesday when it got down here from Chicago. And you know what? If it don't be for this young Leopold cat dropping his glasses at the gully where they stuffed this Frank kid's body, they don't *never* find out who done it."

Mr. Beefer Jones was a man, I discovered, who could explain anything—natural or supernatural. He would always start with:

"If it don't be for. . . ."

I was also to find out later that—no matter what his shortcomings—he was genuinely fond of his two nephews and always boasting about them.

I heard him tell Papa once, when he asked how Sam and James were getting along in the Fourth Grade at the Booker T. Washington Colored Grammar School:

"Smartest boys in the class. Other boys make a hundred; Sam and James make a hundred and ten."

And nowhere in Hopkinsville—or all Christian County, for that matter—could you find two cousins so little like each other.[3]

Sam was a smooth chocolate brown with wavy, almost white folks' hair. He was always laughing and joking and couldn't hold a grudge if you put two handles on it. One time I saw him fight Knee-Baby Watkins to a bloody faretheewell in the school yard just before the bell summoned us into our morning session. And yet, when Miss Annabelle Breckinridge let us out for noon recess, there was Sam offering Knee-Baby half of his pig foot sandwich! (Now everybody knows how hard it is to divide a pig foot sandwich. Especially one made with corn bread.)

But James was just the opposite. James was black and nappy-headed. And he was evil. James never had an open fight with anybody, as far as I know. He got his revenge by sneaking around and finding out something bad on somebody. And he'd hoard the information until that somebody did something to him. And then he'd stool-pigeon the item to somebody big enough to give you a whipping for him.

But Mr. Beefer Jones treated his nephews alike in spite of their different dispositions. And I found out why one day when Papa was mildly chiding Mr. Beefer for indulging the boys too much.

"Well, I'll tell you like it is, Professor Poston," he told Papa. "I don't want them boys to have to go through what I went through when I was coming up over in Pembroke. You ought to know, because you was teaching there when I first started school. But even you didn't know.

"We was ten of us, Professor Poston, and we was pretty poor people. But my mammy was a proud woman—too proud to even let on to our neighbors, who would have helped us.

"She boiled our clothes in the same iron pot with the white folks' wash she took in every Monday. And if little Mister Charlie was missing a shirt, or some drawers or an old pair of play pants when the wash went back—well, we needed 'em more than he did.

"And to tell the truth, Professor Poston, there was many days when none of us in that big family ever crushed a crumb. You was teaching there then, and I bet you never guessed how many days I come to school hungry. But if it don't be for my mammy's mother wit, everybody would have found out. But my mammy always kept *one* little piece of meat when there was nothing else to eat in the house. It was a little piece of bacon rind. And on them mornings when we had nothing to eat, my mammy would give each one of us a dipperful of well water, and then rub that bacon rind around our mouths until our lips were good and greasy, and then she'd send us off to school.

"I remember one time that Miss Anna Glass whipped me in the First Grade. She'd already warned me two times about coming to school without washing my face after eating a big greasy breakfast."[4]

But emotion was one thing, and business was another. And Mr. Beefer Jones never got them mixed up. Except for one time.

Sam and I happened to be up there in the Pleasure Emporium the morning it all started.

James wasn't with us that morning. Mr. Beefer—for the third time—had caught him rifling his "cut box"—the cigar box where Mr. Beefer dropped his nickels and dimes out of each pot—the night before, and had tanned James' hide good and ordered him to stay in the yard for the next two days.

So only me and Sam were there with all the big gamblers from Clarksville, Madisonville, and even from Louisville, that historic morning. These big-time gamblers always came to Hopkinsville on Saturday mornings—right after the tobacco and railroad track workers got paid off. Most of them dressed like Mr. Smoky Smith—black serge britches, washed out blue jumpers and Stetson hats without a crease anywhere.

And the action was hot and heavy on the pool table in the back room, where Mr. Beefer made his real money. Sheriff Sidney Lanier Jenkins didn't know anything about that crap game on the pool table; he was only shaking Mr. Beefer down for the poker and pitty-pat cuts.

And there sat Mr. Beefer, presiding over the ceremonies.

"Fifty-five cents the man shoots," he called out.

"And a dollar five he shoots," Mr. Beefer murmured if the gambler made his point. But, win or lose, Mr. Beefer dropped his nickel into the cut box. There was never any draws for Mr. Beefer. As I said, it was a big morning, and Sam and I stood politely on the fringes waiting for Mr. Beefer to call a break and brag about how the nickels he always gave to his nephews and "Professor Poston's littlest boy" were keeping him broke.

Also standing there, but taking no immediate part in the action, was a new big-shot gambler from Clarksville, Tennessee, called Big Dick Walker. He was following each pass, but making no bets then. The word was that Mr. Big Dick Walker would never make a bet unless the stake was over two hundred dollars.

No bet had reached that high yet, but the action was swift.

"I bet twenty-five-o-five," one shooter was calling out.

"Let him go," the fader shouted, and the shooter came out with a bright seven.[5]

"Fifty-five-o-five," the shooter said.

"Let him go," said another fader—to his sorrow. The shooter came back with an eleven.

But this was old stuff to me and Sam. We'd seen it all before, including the hustling of Go-for Jones (no relation to Mr. Beefer).

I had heard Mr. Smoky Smith explain to Papa once how Go-for got his name.

"It's just like it says, Professor Poston. He hangs around the game and makes his living by being handy to go for cigarettes, or hot dogs, or beer, for anybody who can't leave the table if the dice is hot."

But mainly, Go-for went for beer.

Go-for Jones made a big thing out of his profession.

"I could get a bucket of beer right across the street at Mr. Higgins' saloon," he always boasted, "but I'm a race man myself. And I ain't about to be standing at the back door of no white man's saloon for him to hand me out no bucket. That's why I go up to Mr. Pete

Postell's Saloon, way up there at Sixth and Virginia. I believe in keeping the money in the race."

Now everybody knew that Go-for went to Mr. Pete Postell's because it was eight blocks away, and this gave Go-for a chance to take eight sips of beer out of every bucket he brought back.

And apparently Go-for made many trips that day before me and Sam got there. For, to the astonishment of everybody, including me and Sam, Go-for reached for the dice after Mr. Smoky Smith crapped out.

"A dollar five I shoot," he called out.

And Mr. Smoky Smith, after recovering from his surprise, said, "Let him go."

Go-for came out with a ten, and then made it the hard way—two fives.

"Two-five I shoot," he yelled, and promptly made it.

Then to me and Sam's disgust (Bronco Billy Anderson had surely been shown once by then at the Rex Theater) Mr. Beefer Jones took up the chant.

"Four-five the man shoots," he said, dropping his third nickel into the cut-box, as Go-for came out with a four and made that the hard way too—two deuces.

Go-for kept on passing, to the increasing disgust of me and Sam. What the dickens! Bronco Billy had probably killed ten white bandits by this time, and his colored sidekick, Pistol Pete, had surely been permitted to make several Indians hit the dust.

But I have to admit that even we were a bit shook up when we heard Mr. Beefer Jones chant:

"Two hundred-o-five the man shoots."

There was stunned and chaotic silence around the pool table, for the staggeringly drunk Go-for had wiped out every living human, it seemed.

But into the silence came the voice of the then untested Big Dick Walker from Clarksville.

"Let him go, you all," said Big Dick Walker.

And Go-for came out with an eleven.

Every head swiveled to Big Dick Walker. And he *calmly* said, before ducking for the door and the L. & N. railroad tracks pointing toward Clarksville:

"I told you to let that jigaboo *go*. He's too hot for me!"

Go-for only chased him as far as Pembroke, I heard later, but he came back the next day and told Mr. Beefer Jones that *he*, as game runner, owed him four hundred dollars. Mr. Beefer Jones pointed out, quite logically, that Go-for had not waited to see his money actually faded before he'd come out with that hot eleven. So, therefore, the house was not responsible.

"As a matter of fact," Mr. Beefer Jones said, "you still got the dice, Go-for. What do you shoot?"

And Go-for stuck his hand out and made the remark which gave him a new nickname. He said simply: "Set the meat outdoors!"[6]

Mr. Beefer Jones paid him his two hundred dollars in cash, and Set-the-Meat promptly went down to Mr. Dan Metzler's Cut-Rate Store and spent every penny of it on the first store-bought clothes he'd ever had in his life.

Of course, he almost starved to death the next two weeks. But what man dressed that well could afford to be hustling beers for a bunch of lousy gamblers?

The whole matter might have ended right there—if James Wilkes hadn't been let out of the yard two days later.

Having heard of the whole affair from me and Sam, he went straight to Set-the-Meat (formerly Go-for) and told him:

"Sheriff Sidney Lanier Jenkins don't know nothing about Uncle Beefer's crap game. Why don't you go and tell him? Maybe Sheriff Jenkins will make him give up that two hundred dollars that Big Dick Walker called you for."

I only learned about this later when Mr. Beefer Jones came up home to Papa and asked him what he should do about Sheriff Sidney Lanier Jenkins' demand for two thousand five hundred dollars in back bribery.

"If it don't be for I got that much set aside, I wouldn't be worried," he told Papa, "but if I give it to him, I got to start again from scratch. And since Set-the-Meat and I ain't speaking now, who's going to hustle the beer around the table?"

Papa, as usual, considered the matter in his judicial manner. Then he said:

"Aren't you forgetting something, Orlando? Sheriff Jenkins got defeated in the April fourth election. He goes out of office next month. So why don't you take Mrs. Beth back up to Chicago for a month's visit with her folks? You can always come back when Mr. Sidney Lanier Jenkins is a private citizen."

Mr. Beefer thanked Papa profusely and not only went to Chicago with Aunt Beth, but he took Sam and James with him.

And he never came back. This was a great disappointment to a lot of people (including me every time I wanted to go to the Rex Theater or to top everybody else in the Sunday School collection).

But Mr. Smoky Smith, who spent every summer vacation up in Chicago, told Papa he had run across Mr. Beefer Jones one time up there.

"And he said to me, Professor Poston," Mr. Smoky Smith said, "'I would have come back to Hop'town if it don't be for the sheriff up *here* only charges me *fifteen* dollars a week—and that includes the crap game cuts, too.'"

7

HIGH ON THE HOG

Tack-Haired Baker's country cousin, Mr. Fertilizer Ferguson, was the last man in the world—not to mention Hopkinsville, Ky.— who could have been expected to make a lasting contribution to the vividness of American expression.[1]

For, although he was already past middle age, or so it seemed to us when Tack and I first entered the Booker T. Washington Colored Grammar School, Mr. Ferguson could hardly read or write his own name.

But his lasting contribution to American self-expression was not the reason the white folks remembered Mr. Fertilizer Ferguson. They always recalled him—with a shudder—as the man who once almost bankrupted the whole community of Christian County.

Now me, I remembered him for neither of these reasons. In the first place, his contribution to the language had been made years before I was born. And the shudders he sent through the financial fibre of Hopkinsville, Ky., were still to come when I first became aware of the existence of Mr. Fertilizer Ferguson.

I remembered him for one reason only. He was the first man I ever saw who possibly could have been darker than my Uncle John Braxton.

I had heard of Mr. Ferguson before I met him. Although Papa and Mama thought I was asleep the night they were discussing him.

"He is so black," Papa was telling Mama, although he knew that she did not relish discussions of color complexes among our colored citizens, "that he is almost beautiful. He is a sort of translucent blue instead of black."

But none of this helped me in my unending dispute on the question with Tack-Haired Baker in the Booker T. Washington Colored Grammar School.

For Tack insisted that my Uncle John was *blacker* than his cousin, Mr. Fertilizer Ferguson.

It was obvious that Tack was taking this position out of family pride. So I was willing to concede that on an overall basis, he might be right.

I admitted that, on pound-to-pound analysis, there might be more black in Uncle John, because Uncle John weighed 365 pounds to Mr. Ferguson's 145. But I always added:

"But if you take any one square inch off of either of them and hold it up to the light, you'll have to admit that your cousin, Mr. Fertilizer Ferguson, is three times as black as my Uncle John."

Of course we were never really able to make this simple test. For color comparison was a forbidden subject for discussion among our older colored citizens.

In fact, Tack and I were breaking an unwritten covenant in even discussing the matter between us. For although the quality from which he derived his name gave him certain privileges, Tack could almost have been classified as a high yaller himself.

But our fellow classmate, Rat Joiner of Billy Goat Hill, practically gave Tack a passport into our intimate circle one day when he observed:

"Reuben, you undoubtedly got the nappiest head of hair in Hopkinsville, Ky. You are the only man I know that's even got nappy eyebrows."

Rat pondered the problem for another minute, and then said:

"It could be because your yaller skin shines through the top. But I swear your hair looks like carpet tacks on a linoleum kitchen floor."

From that moment on, Reuben was Tack-Haired Baker.

And it was cinched the next day when Rat, after a night's consideration of the matter, added:

"I swear, Reuben, them naps of yours are so tight that they look like a bunch of Mexican mice titties."

But the fact that both our relatives were rather dark—and that both wound up later as relatively rich men—were the only two things that Uncle John and Mr. Fertilizer Ferguson had in common. For Uncle John was fat and fun-loving. And Mr. Fertilizer (whose real name was Isaiah, I discovered years later) was skinny and a skinflint. And Uncle John became rich almost accidentally. Mr. Fertilizer did it on purpose.

They both owned farms—at least they held the titles while the First Tobacco and Planters' Trust Company really owned them—about 14 miles from Hopkinsville.

And Uncle John (and Aunt Fanny and all my seven cousins) starved to death for 30 years trying to meet the mortgage payments, until the white folks found out that Uncle John could barbecue a pig better than anyone else on God's green earth. And although he had been doing that free of charge at family reunions for a couple of generations, the white folks finally insisted upon paying him for doing the same thing for them out at the Hopkinsville Country Club.

And Uncle John found himself getting rich almost against his will with the title of "Barbecue Poet Laureate of the State of Kentucky."[2]

(I remember once that some white folks came down to a golf tournament in Hopkinsville and set up an "Uncle John's Day" in Lansing, Michigan. The whole thing almost blew up in their faces, though, because they forgot to tell Uncle John that they were going to *fly* him up there for the barbecue celebration.

(It finally came off all right though. For, at Uncle John's insistence, they put the whole thing back five days so that Uncle John could make the trip from Hopkinsville to Lansing, Michigan, by bus. Uncle John wouldn't even trust a railroad train with his 365 pounds—much less an airplane.)

Now Mr. Fertilizer Ferguson (although his name was not Fertilizer then) was absolutely different.

From the minute that he and Uncle John put their first $100

down payment on their adjoining farms many years before I was born, Mr. Fertilizer started figuring on how he would get off his. And Mr. Fertilizer could figure.

He studied our colored community in Hopkinsville, Kentucky, for instance, and came up with a startling discovery.

It was this: Although many of our leading colored citizens still maintained a taste for pigs' feet, chitterlings, hog maw, and all such delicacies, they were reluctant to ask for them at the Piggly Wiggly stores and other shopping centers.

Even I had heard Mrs. Nixola Green, our local society leader, say:

"If there is one thing I can't stand, it is to see Negroes going to the store and asking white folks for things like watermelon, fried chicken, pigs' feet and chitterlings. Such Negroes might very well still be in slavery, so far as I am concerned."

So Mr. Fertilizer Ferguson immediately put two and two together, and it added up to this: it was that our leading colored citizens still loved pigs' feet and chitterlings; they only became traitors to the race when they purchased these delicacies in public from the white folks.

So Mr. Isaiah Ferguson (later to become Fertilizer) was in business.

Instead of planting tobacco, like Uncle John did, and starving to death, he started rounding up every trotter (the local expression for pigs' feet) that wasn't attached to the living organism.

And, as soon as he had a couple of dozen in hand, he hotfooted it to Hopkinsville and peddled them at the back doors of our leading colored citizens.

And during the course of his business, Mr. Fertilizer Ferguson made another startling discovery. It was this: Many of our leading quality white folks loved pigs' feet, chitterlings and hog maw too. And they also were too proud to shop for them in the public markets.

So Mr. Fertilizer Ferguson's business doubled.

And this eventually led to his unique contribution to the American art of self-expression.

For the big farmer next door, a white man named Mr. Acre,

married a town white lady who had read all of the pre–Civil War novels and she always insisted on calling their farm a plantation.

Mr. Acre just called it a hog farm, because he was in the business of supplying the Higgins' Packing Company in Hopkinsville most of its pork products.

But, because there was little call from the public markets for pigs' feet and chitterlings, he usually threw these commodities away as he concentrated on breakfast bacon, hams, spareribs and shoulders.

And this gave Mrs. Acre an opportunity to expand her picture of romantic plantation life. Every Sunday she invited all of her young white matron friends out from Hopkinsville, so that she could watch for Mr. Fertilizer Ferguson on his way back from the Bethel Baptist Church services.

And then, fanning herself on the front porch like a true Southern belle, she would call out to Mr. Fertilizer (as her town friends listened):

"Oh, Isaiah. Mr. Acre just had another slaughter this weekend. And we've got several bushels of pigs' feet which he's planning to throw out. If you want to, you can take them down to Bessie (Mrs. Fertilizer) and the children. I just hate to see them thrown away."[3]

And Mr. Fertilizer always answered:

"Thankee, Mrs. Acre. Thankee very much."

But Mrs. Bessie nor none of her 14 children ever gritted a gum on a single one of those early trotters. Mr. Fertilizer was too busy selling them to our leading colored and white citizens.

And business became so good that within four years—while Uncle John, Aunt Fanny and their progeny were starving to death on an adjacent 100 acres—Mr. Fertilizer was able to sell his unfarmed farm at a profit over what he'd agreed to pay for it.

He had come back to pick up assorted odds and ends that last Sunday when Mrs. Acre hailed him as he drove by in his brand new tin lizzie Ford.

"Oh, Isaiah," she hailed him as usual (as her town friends looked on patronizingly), "Mr. Acre had another slaughter this weekend, and we've got several bushels of pigs' feet which he was planning to throw out . . ."

And it was then that Mr. Fertilizer Ferguson made his undeniable dent on the English language. For Mr. Fertilizer said: "Thankee, Mrs. Acre. I appreciate all you did for me. But, Isaiah is eating a little higher up on the hog these days."

Some carping critics among our colored citizens insisted that Mr. Fertilizer Ferguson was really showing off when he coined that lasting American expression.

Nobody doubted his ability to eat higher up on the hog, for no one ever saw Mr. Ferguson spend money for anything that he could get free of charge. In fact, some of them insisted that Mr. Fertilizer later stuffed his own family so full of free pigs' feet that his oldest boys learned to grunt before they could talk.

But Mr. Ferguson moved into town so that he could enlarge his operations. First he made contracts with the Dixie Cafe, Hotel Latham and several boarding houses to remove their garbage daily free of charge.[4]

He then went back out to Mr. Acre's hog farm and offered to bring the slop out daily to feed Mr. Acre's pigs. In return for this, Mr. Fertilizer was given free and exclusive rights to all the pigs' feet, chitterlings and hog maw from Mr. Acre's weekly slaughter. And before anybody knew exactly what was going on, Mr. Fertilizer Ferguson was not only peddling pigs' feet all over Hopkinsville, but his three younger boys were doing the same thing at some of the better back doors in Pembroke, Clarksville, and even as far away as Paducah, Kentucky.

This activity would have satisfied any ordinary citizen. But not Mr. Ferguson.

He bought himself three more sets of mules and three broken-down dirt wagons and then signed a contract with the city to take over its sanitary disposal. Our sewer system had not been put in then, even in those exclusive sections where our quality white folks lived, and Mr. Ferguson's new project prospered from the beginning.

Of course, there were some objections from some longstanding pigs' feet customers, but Mr. Ferguson put their doubts at rest. He assured each one that there was no connection between his sanitary business and his pigs' feet business.

"My two oldest boys handle the sanitary business," I once heard him assure Mama, "and I don't even let them touch the wagons I use for my farm products business. Fact is, they don't even live at home. I got them a place out on Billy Goat Hill."

Our elders accepted this explanation, but there were always doubts in my mind and in Tack-Haired Baker's and Rat Joiner's also. For we sat in the Fourth Grade with little Fertilizer, Jr. And young Fert always seemed a bit more fragrant than necessary.

As the years rolled by, it was inevitable that reports would crop up that Mr. Fertilizer Ferguson was becoming a very wealthy man. Not that he gave any outward evidence of it. Fert, Jr., and all his other children were always clean and tidy, but Rat Joiner insisted that any suit Mr. Ferguson purchased for his oldest son ended up with seven wearers eventually before it worked its way down to little Fert, Jr.

Smoky Smith, our leading colored sporting man, said that common sense made him know that Mr. Ferguson was a rich man.

"He ain't spent a nickel for nothing he didn't have to since Hector was a pup," Smoky insisted. "He's got to be loaded."

But Papa and Mr. Ed Smith, our leading colored undertaker, were a little taken aback when Mr. Fertilizer Ferguson brought the matter to them himself.

"Professor Poston," he said to Papa, "you got book learning, and I wonder if you and Mr. Smith would give me some advice."

They readily agreed, but Mr. Ferguson beat around the bush for so long that they finally had to make him come to the point. And finally he told them:

"I been a hard-working man and I've laid a couple of nickels by for me and my old lady's old age.

"Well, the other night somebody was out there digging in my barn and out behind my chicken coop. I believe they were trying to steal my few nickels, and I want you all to tell me what to do about it."

"If you've got any money, Isaiah," Papa said, "you should put it in the bank. It is not only a question of somebody robbing you, but your house might burn down or something and you'd lose everything you got."

Mr. Ed Smith seconded the motion. "I know Mr. Beauregard Jones who is President of the First Tobacco and Planters' Trust Company," he said, "and I'd be glad to introduce him to a new customer."

But neither Papa nor Mr. Smith was prepared for what they found when they went out to his house to help Mr. Fertilizer Ferguson count his money.

Papa was still breathless when he told Mama about it that night while I was doing my arithmetic lesson under the dining room table.

"You won't believe it, Mama," he said, "but do you know how much money that Isaiah Ferguson has buried in a big iron kettle under his lean-to kitchen?"

Papa caught his breath and then pronounced the sum in awe.

"More than *twenty* thousand dollars," he said. "More money than I ever saw or hoped to see in cash in this life."

Naturally they stayed out there until after dark and then brought the money back to town where they locked it up in Mr. Ed Smith's office safe until they could take it to the bank in the morning. And Mr. Fertilizer Ferguson sat on top of that safe with his shotgun all night long.

"Ed was a little put out at Isaiah insisting on staying there," Papa recalled, "and I didn't think it was fair for him to tell Isaiah that he had two corpses back in the embalming room.

"But Isaiah just said: 'It ain't the dead ones I'm worried about, Mr. Ed. It's the live ones I got to look out for tonight.'"

And Mr. Beauregard Jones almost had a heart attack himself when Papa and Mr. Ed Smith marched Mr. Fertilizer Ferguson into the First Tobacco and Planters' Trust Company and dumped

$20,000 in mildewed $1, $5 and $10 bills out of an old grass sack Mr. Ferguson was carrying.

Papa and Mr. Ed Smith tried to keep the matter quiet, but somehow or other the story got out. And Mr. Fertilizer Ferguson found himself a very popular man in our colored community. He had to stop personally peddling his pigs' feet at some of the sporting houses because the girls started making calf eyes at him.

The glamor even rubbed off on other members of his family. As Rat Joiner put it:

"You know what? That stinking little Fert, Jr., is beginning to smell better every day."

The saga of Mr. Fertilizer Ferguson might have ended right there if Mr. Beauregard Jones had not gone into semi-retirement a few years later. And if they had not brought some snippy young white man from Nashville, Tenn., to run the First Tobacco and Planters' Trust Company bank.

And it was just Mr. Ferguson's luck that he was the first colored customer in the bank the day the new man took over.

And he was boiling with indignation that summer morning when he rushed out home for an emergency conference with Papa and Mr. Ed Smith.

"You know I don't bother nobody, Professor Poston," he said, "and nobody can call me uppidy. Well, that little snip that took Mr. Beauregard's place jumped on me like a duck on a june-bug the minute I went in there today.

"He called me 'boy'—and I started to ask him how big did boys grow down in Nashville, Tenn.[5] But I didn't. And then he said I had to pull my hat off when I came in *his* bank.

"Now I don't think this is right, Professor Poston. And I want you and Mr. Ed to tell me what to do."

Papa pondered the problem in his usual deliberate manner and then asked: "How much money you got in that bank, Isaiah?"

And Mr. Fertilizer seemed suddenly embarrassed.

"I think I got me 'bout $53,000 and some cents," he finally

mumbled, "at least that's what my oldest boy says it says in the books."

Papa and Mr. Ed Smith were almost speechless.

"But you only had $20,000 when we counted it . . ." Mr. Ed Smith said, but Mr. Fertilizer had decided on a full confession.

"Well, when you all first talked me into this," he said, "I wasn't so sure about banks. So I only showed you what I had in *one* kettle. But after I got to know Mr. Beauregard so well, I dug up the other one and put that in the bank too."

Papa and Mr. Ed Smith were a bit exasperated—especially Mr. Ed—but they immediately tackled the higher principle involved.

"Why, Isaiah," Papa said, "you've probably got more money in that bank than Mr. Beauregard Jones himself. And no snip has any business talking to you like that."

He and Mr. Ed Smith went over to the other side of the porch and conferred a few minutes, and then they told Mr. Fertilizer Ferguson:

"The *Daily Kentucky New Era* said they are going to name some new directors for the First Tobacco and Planters' Trust Company. Now you go down there and tell that little snip how much money you got in that bank. And tell him you want to be a director since you are one of the largest depositors."

Mr. Ferguson seemed a little doubtful at first, but Papa and Mr. Ed Smith finally talked him into it.

He left in a huff to head straight for the bank. But he was back on our front porch an hour later. Not only had the new little snip laughed in his face when he said he wanted to be a director, he had called the janitor and practically had Mr. Fertilizer Ferguson thrown out.

"So what do I do now?" he said.

Papa told him. And bright and early the next morning, Papa, Mr. Ed Smith, Mr. Fertilizer Ferguson and lawyer Orvil Coldweather, our colored counselor, all marched into the First Tobacco and Planters' Trust Company bank.

And all three of them helped Mr. Ferguson fill out a withdrawal slip for the flat sum of $53,121.13, to close out the account of our most prosperous citizen.

The little snip from Nashville thought they were joking at first. But when Mr. Fertilizer Ferguson pulled out his deposit books and showed he had exactly $53,121.13 in the bank, the little snip almost fainted.

First he tried to put them off. But Mr. Ferguson wouldn't be put off. Then he said he didn't have that much money on the premises. And Mr. Ferguson said: "Gimme what you got and I'll come back and pick up the rest later."

And then the little snip got so excited, he rushed out and locked the bank door from the inside while he tried to telephone Mr. Beauregard Jones up in Louisville where he was living with his daughter.

But Mr. Beauregard Jones was out fishing, and the snip, finally in desperation, telephoned Judge Hezekiah Witherspoon, our city's veteran Republican leader.

Judge Witherspoon closed down court and rushed right over, but even he couldn't budge Mr. Fertilizer Ferguson.

"It said in the book I could get my money on demand," Mr. Ferguson said: "Well, I'm sorry, Judge, but I demand—right now."

They were still arguing about it at noon, and when several prospective depositors came by and found the bank doors locked from the inside, they spread word around that something must be wrong.

Judge Witherspoon had feared that something like that would happen, so at 1 P.M., he told the little snip to give Mr. Fertilizer Ferguson his money.

The snip obeyed Judge Witherspoon's order, but it took practically every cent they could beg, steal, and borrow to raise the whole amount. And the bank didn't open again for three days as they had to send to Nashville to get some fresh money.

But Papa, Mr. Ed Smith, lawyer Orvil Coldweather and Mr. Fertilizer Ferguson all marched in a body to Mr. Ed Smith's undertaking parlor where they put the money in the office safe. And all of them sat there guarding it until early the next day.

Judge Witherspoon himself came by the office and tried to get Mr. Ferguson to invest his money in some Illinois Central Railroad stock which the Judge was selling on commission.

And Judge Witherspoon not only arranged for Mr. Ferguson and his whole family to take the next train out for Chicago; Judge Witherspoon went up with them and even rode in the Jim Crow car with them as far as Evansville, Ind.

We never saw Mr. Fertilizer Ferguson again in Hopkinsville. But Papa ran into him once up in Chicago. Papa said he was still making money although his business now was real estate.

Mr. Ferguson liked Chicago just fine, Papa said, but he didn't think much of the leading colored citizens up there.

"They ain't got no race pride, Professor Poston," Mr. Fertilizer Ferguson told Papa.

"Why, they go right down to these white folks' stores and purchase pigs' feet, chitterlings and hog maw right out in public. I'm sure that Mr. Armour, Mr. Cudahy and the other quality white folks up here don't really respect them.

"I know Mr. Acre never would have. The idea! Buying pigs' feet out in public."

THE BIRTH
OF A NOTION

There had never been a Ku Klux Klan in Hopkinsville, Ky. So it was sort of surprising how our leading colored citizens got all worked up when they heard that "The Birth of a Nation" was coming to the Rex Theater down on Ninth Street.[1]

It was we young ones who brought them the news—although it didn't mean anything to us. And it was we young ones who got them out of it when the situation finally reached a stalemate.

The whole thing started one Saturday morning when Bronco Billy Anderson was being featured at the Rex in "The Revenge of the Ranger." And of course not a one of us could afford to miss that.

Naturally, the Booker T. Washington Colored Grammar School was not open on Saturdays, but that meant only one extra hour's sleep. For all of us had to be at the Rex at 9:00 A.M. to be sure that we could get front row seats in the peanut gallery which was reserved for all of our colored citizens.

It was absolutely essential that we be there when the doors opened or else the bigger boys would get there first and take the choice front row seats.

We always thought the big boys were unfair, but there was nothing we could do about it. No self-respecting young colored citizen would dream of squealing to the white folks about it. And furthermore, if we did, we knew the big boys would bop us over our heads for doing it.

But this was our problem: The Rex Theater charged only 5 cents admission for all of our young colored citizens under 10 years of age. But since the white ticket lady who took our nickels was near-sighted, and had only a small peephole through which to see us as we stood in the alley for our gallery seats, there was a *rumor* around the colored community that none of us grew any older after we were nine years old until we suddenly reached 21 or more.

For all you had to do was bend your knees, look up innocently, and slip your nickel through the slot, and she'd pass you right up the gallery stairs. After all, her peephole was very small and she couldn't see anything but your face anyway.

There was a rumor—which I never believed—that Jelly Roll Benson never paid more than a nickel to get into the Rex until he was 35 years old.[2]

"That's why he walks with a stoop in his shoulders and a bend in his knees to this day," Rat Joiner always insisted. "He got that way from fooling Miss Lucy (the ticket lady).[3]

"He'd still be doing it now, but he forgot to shave one morning. And she suspected for the first time that he was over 10."

But all this happened before that historic Saturday when we all rushed there to see Bronco Billy Anderson in "The Revenge of the Ranger." All of us were crazy about Bronco Billy, but there was really another reason for going to see him also.

For in every picture, Bronco Billy's main sidekick was a cow-boy named Buffalo Pete. And, believe it or not, Buffalo Pete was as highly visible and 100 per cent colored as any citizen up on Billy Goat Hill.

He was the only colored cowboy or colored anything we ever saw in the movies those days, and we wouldn't think of missing him. Our enthusiasm was not even dimmed by the cynicism of Rat Joiner, who observed one day:

"They don't never let him kill none of them white mens, no mat-ter how evil they is. Oh yeah, they let him knock off a Indian every now and then. But only Bronco Billy kills them white bad mens."

(There was an unconfirmed rumor around town that another movie actor named Noble Johnson had Negro blood. But we didn't pay that no mind. We figured that the high yallers in our colored community had dreamed up that story for prestige purposes. And anyway, Noble Johnson played in those silly love stories they showed at the Rex on weekday nights. And who would pay 5 cents to see one of them?)

But back to "The Revenge of the Ranger" that Saturday. It was a real knockdown picture and we saw it eight times before they put us out at 5 P.M. in order to let the grownups in for the evening (at 15 cents a head).

And there was one big scene at the end where everybody was shooting in which Buffalo Pete might very well have killed one of those white bad men—Rat Joiner notwithstanding.

We got downstairs and out of the alley at just about the same time that the little white boys were being put out also, and we noticed that they were all carrying handbills in their fists.

Nobody had passed out any handbills upstairs, but we had no difficulty getting some when we found out that Tack-Haired Baker had been paid 25 cents to stand by the front door in the lobby and pass them out.

We were a little disappointed when we read them, because it didn't mean anything to us then. Bronco Billy and Buffalo Pete weren't even mentioned anywhere on the handbills. They read:

Special! Special! Special!
THE SOUTH RISES AGAIN!
Come see D. W. Griffith's:
"THE BIRTH OF A NATION"
(Based on "The Clansman")
Every night—Tuesday Through Friday.
Admission 25 cents.

Most of us threw the handbills away before we got home, and I don't remember how I happened to hold onto mine.

But I still had it in my hand when I climbed up our front steps and tried to wend my way through the usual Saturday crowd of elders and sporting men who were holding their weekly session with Papa. Papa was Professor E. Poston, Dean of Men at Kentucky State Industrial College for Negroes in Frankfort and the official arbiter of all bets and disputes which piled up during his two-weekly absences from home.

My sister Lillian who was only three years older than I was showing off by sitting next to Papa (as he explained that a Negro jockey named Isaac Murphy was the first man to ride three winners in the Kentucky Derby in 1884, 1890 and 1891). So as I stepped around Smoky Smith, our leading colored gambling man who had raised the question, I handed Lillian the handbill. This "Birth of a Nation" thing sounded like one of those silly love story movies she was always going to, so I thought I was doing her a favor.

But I was absolutely unprepared for the commotion that was raised when Mr. Freddie Williams, the first deacon of our Virginia Street Baptist Church, happened to glance at the handbill and let out a screech.

"Don't that say 'The Birth of a Nation'?" he yelled as he snatched it out of Lillian's hands. "And coming to the Rex Theater here?"

He thrust the crumpled handbill in Papa's face and said:

"Professor Poston, you've got to do something about this right away."

Papa read the handbill carefully as even the sporting men started grumbling but I still believe there was a half grin in his eyes although his mouth seemed severe.

I still had no idea what had caused the commotion, but Mr. J. B. Petty, our local insurance man–historian, very soon put me right.

It seemed that this novel, "The Clansman," and the moving picture "The Birth of a Nation" were something about a bunch of peckerwoods who dressed up in sheets and went around whipping the heads of unsuspecting colored citizens and yelling about something called white supremacy. And there was one place in both things about some Negro—"played by a white man," Mr. J. B. Petty explained—who chased some poor white woman off the top of a rock quarry, with her yelling "Death before dishonor," whatever that meant.

But Mr. Freddie Williams was putting it right up to Papa.

"You know what it will mean to show this sort of thing to those hillbillies and peckerwoods around here, Professor Poston," he kept saying. "And I'm sure that the quality white folks will agree with you if you put it up to them right. I'm surprised that Mr. Max Kaplan (who owned the Rex) even thought of letting this happen."

Now even I knew that Mr. Max Kaplan was not exactly quality white folks in the eyes of Hopkinsville, Kentucky, even if he was a very popular white citizen in the colored community.

And neither was Judge Hezekiah Witherspoon, our veteran Republican leader, quality either. But he ran Hopkinsville, Ky., and it was to him that the group decided that Papa should make his first appeal.

Papa went right down to see him that Saturday night, but the meeting wasn't altogether successful.

As I heard Papa explaining it to Mama when he finally got home, Judge Witherspoon started talking about private enterprise and what were the Negroes excited about anyhow? But Papa had one more weapon up his sleeve, he explained to Mama.

"So I finally said to him," (Papa recalled) "'I don't know if you read the book, Judge Witherspoon, but the whole thing is about the terrible things the scalawags and carpetbaggers did to the people of the South during Reconstruction.

"'And although I didn't want to mention the subject, Judge, you must remember that all of those scalawags and carpetbaggers were Republicans, so I wonder if you want people reminded of that?'"

Papa chuckled as he recalled Judge Witherspoon's reaction.

"'Eph, you damn' Democrat,' he yelled at me," Papa said. "'You keep your politics out of this.' But I could see that he was shaken, and I just let him rave for a few minutes.

"But finally he said: 'I'm not gonna get mixed up in this thing. But you go and see Max Kaplan and tell him how our colored citizens feel about this thing. And tell him I'll back him up if he feels he's got to do something about it.'"

Papa was very set up about the meeting. "I'm going out to see

Mr. Max Kaplan tomorrow morning. After all, Sunday is not his Sabbath and he won't be adverse to talking a little business."

I still didn't quite understand what the shouting was all about. But I had no doubt that Mr. Max Kaplan would side with our colored citizens if Papa asked him to.

For Mr. Max Kaplan was quite an unusual citizen even in Hopkinsville, Ky. He had come there years before I was born and had got into hot water the minute he built the Rex Theater, because he had planned only ground floor seats for white and colored citizens alike.

Of course, the white folks, including the quality ones, had beaten him down on that, and he had been forced to spend extra money to fix the peanut gallery up for us.

(Reaching Pete Washington, a classmate of mine in the Booker T. Washington Colored Grammar School, once said he was glad Mr. Max Kaplan lost that fight. Reaching Pete didn't have a nickel one Saturday when "The Clutching Hand" serial was playing the Rex, so he kept on up the alley and slipped through the fire escape door on the ground floor where the white folks sat.

(It was dark, of course, and nobody noticed that Reaching Pete had slipped in. But everybody knew it a few minutes later. For when Pete looked up, he was right under the screen and the pictures were 20 feet tall. And just at that moment, the Clutching Hand, a very mean crook who had a claw for his right hand, was reaching out for his next victim, and Pete thought he was reaching for him.

(Pete closed his eyes and screamed so loud that they had to turn on the lights in the whole theater to find out what was going on. The cops wanted to lock Reaching Pete up, but Mr. Max Kaplan wouldn't let them. He even let Reaching Pete go upstairs free of charge.)

But that wasn't the only thing that endeared Mr. Max Kaplan to our colored community. There was the matter of Tapper Johnson, our motion picture projectionist.

When the white folks balked Mr. Max Kaplan and made him

build a whole peanut gallery for our colored citizens (after starting a whispering campaign that he was trying to bring his New York City ideas to Hopkinsville) he made up his mind to get even.

So he decided to make his most highly paid employee in the whole enterprise one of our colored citizens. That was when he hired Tapper and trained him to be the only moving picture machine operator in all of Hopkinsville. And he paid Tapper $35 each and every week.

And Tapper paid Mr. Max Kaplan back real nice too. He became the best moving picture operator for his size and age in all of Kentucky, and there were rumors that he could have gotten $5 more a week in Clarksville, Tenn., if Mr. Kaplan had ever given him a vacation or a day off to go see about it.

But Tapper didn't want a day off. He had only two loves in his life—his motion picture machine, and little Cecelia Penrod with whom he had been in love long before he quit the Fourth Grade in the Booker T. Washington Colored Grammar School.

His love affair with the Rex Theater moving picture machine went along smoothly. But not his love affair with little Cecelia. For Cecelia was one of the nieces of Mrs. Nixola Green, our high yaller social leader. And she felt that Tapper was too dark to become a member of her family or of her secret Blue Vein Society.

In fact, my sister Lillian was always saying that Mrs. Nixola was trying to marry Cecelia off to Pat Slaker (who naturally was yaller), but that Pat and Cecelia weren't paying each other any mind. Cecelia was in love with Tapper, Lillian said, although there wasn't much she could do about it. She never got to go to the Rex Theater alone. Mrs. Nixola always insisted on accompanying her.

Papa probably had all this in mind that Sunday morning when he hopefully set out for Mr. Max Kaplan's home. But Papa was in for a disappointment. Mr. Kaplan wasn't in town. He'd left three weeks ago for California where—some white citizens insisted—friends of his were running this whole movie business from some suburb near Los Angeles. And he wasn't expected home until Wednesday.

Now "The Birth of a Nation" was due to start running Tuesday night. So time became of the essence as the elders of Freeman (Methodist) Chapel and Virginia Street Baptist Church met that afternoon to receive Papa's report.

"Professor Poston," Mr. Freddie Williams finally said after the discussion had gone on for hours, "I know how you feel about poor white trash. But with Mr. Max Kaplan out of town, there's nothing we can do but appeal to S. J. Bolton, Mr. Kaplan's manager of the Rex."

It took some talking on the part of the elders, but Papa was finally persuaded to lay the matter before Mr. S. J. Bolton. And the results were disastrous, as he reported it to Mama later.

"This clay-eating cracker," Papa said later, in as near an approach to profanity as he permitted himself, "had the nerve to call me Eph. He said to me: 'Eph, what are you Nigras upset about? Why, my grandfather was one of the founders of the Clan. No Nigra who knows his place has anything to worry about on this glorious story of the re-rise of the South.'

"And then he added," Papa said, "'Why, Eph, you must know what my initials, S.J., stand for. It's Stonewall Jackson Bolton, of course.'"

Papa's indignation at the outcome of his conference was far exceeded by the reaction of the elders who met on our lawn that Sunday afternoon to hear his report.

But none of us young ones felt personally involved until Mr. Freddie Williams summed up the feelings of the elders.

"All right," he said, "if that is the way the white folks feel about it, let them. But I move that if 'The Birth of a Nation' opens at the Rex Tuesday evening, then the 'Death of the Rex' should set in that very night. Because if we don't patronize that peanut gallery Mr. Max Kaplan has for us, then they ain't gonna make enough money each week to pay even Tapper's salary. And that means not only us staying away, but our kids as well—Bronco Billy and Buffalo Pete notwithstanding."

79

Now this created a very desperate situation indeed, as I explained to my classmates at the Booker T. Washington Colored Grammar School the next morning.

But what could we young tads do about it? We were all pretty downcast until Rat said:

"I think I got a birth of a notion."

"Nation," I amended, a bit sullenly.

"Naw, notion," said Rat Joiner. And then he explained.

And as soon as school was out that day, we all went to work to raise the 15 cents Rat said was necessary for the success of his plan. Coca Cola bottles, scrap wire, everything went into the pot until the 15 cents was raised.

There was no picket line at the Rex the next night. Although some of our most responsible colored citizens were loitering around the alley from the minute the evening tickets went on sale.

And most of them were very upset when Rat Joiner, the pride of Billy Goat Hill, showed up as the only colored customer that night who planked down 15 cents and requested a peanut gallery ticket from Miss Lucy.

In fact, there was talk about mentioning the fact to Rev. Paul Laurence Dunbar Timberlake, and having him read Roosevelt Alonzo Taylor Joiner out of the congregation of the Dirt's Ave. Methodist Church.

But that was before they found out the nature of Rat's mission.

For Rat entered the Rex just 30 minutes before the main feature was to go on, and just when Tapper was preparing to rewind the film for Hopkinsville's first showing of "The Birth of a Nation."

And after he knocked on the door of the projection room, Rat came right to the matter at hand.

"Tapper," he said, "Mrs. Nixola Green has finally persuaded Cecelia to run off and marry Pat Slaker. They're up at Mrs. Nixola's house on First St. and they're going to head for Clarksville any minute.

"I know it ain't none of my business, but you always been fair to us and. . . ."

Tapper waited to hear no more. He dashed out of the projection room and headed first for Mrs. Nixola's house on First St.

Of course, Cecelia wasn't there, for (as Rat well knew) the whole family was over in Earlington, Ky., attending a family reunion.

But Tapper didn't know this. So he rushed down to Irving's Livery Stable and rented the fastest horse and rig for an emergency dash to Clarksville, Tenn., where he hoped to head off the nuptials.

Well, the downstairs section of the Rex Theater was crowded (with only Rat in the peanut gallery) before Mr. S. J. Bolton learned that Hopkinsville's only movie machine projector was no longer in the Rex Theater.

He tried to stall the showing for a half hour, but when Tapper didn't show up then (he was only halfway to Clarksville by that time) Mr. S. J. Bolton tried to run the machine himself.

Rat, who had decided to stay inside since he had paid an unheard-of 15 cents to be there anyway, explained to us later what happened.

"Tapper had started rewinding the film backward to get to the front," he said, "but Mr. S. J. Bolton didn't know that. So he picked up the first film roll he saw and started running it on that picture thing.

"Well, it turned out that it was the middle of the picture and backwards besides. So, instead of that colored gentleman (played by some white man) chasing that white lady off the top of the quarry, it started with the white lady at the bottom of the quarry. And she was leaping up to the top of the quarry so that the colored gentleman (who was really a white man) could grab her.

"The white folks didn't see much of the picture, because Mr. S. J. Bolton yanked that part off so fast that he tore up the whole thing. I waited around another half hour and nothing else came on, so all of us went home."

There wasn't much else to tell. Mr. Max Kaplan came back the next day and substituted another film, called "East Lynn" or something, for "The Birth of a Nation." There were always two schools of thought in the colored community after that—and even Papa couldn't settle the dispute.

One school held that Mr. Max Kaplan would never have let "The Birth of a Nation" be booked for the Rex if he had known anything about it and if he hadn't been in Los Angeles. And the other school contended that Mr. S. J. Bolton had so messed up the original print in trying to run it without Tapper that it couldn't have been shown anyway.

But Mr. Max Kaplan took steps to see that the situation never happened again. He had little Cecelia Penrod smuggled out of her house that very afternoon while Mrs. Nixola wasn't watching. And he took her and Tapper down to Judge Hezekiah Witherspoon who married both of them on the spot.

So Hopkinsville, Ky., never got to see "The Birth of a Nation."

But Mrs. Nixola Green, who collapsed on the news of Cecelia's marriage to Tapper, went over to Clarksville, Tenn., to recuperate at the home of some of her high yaller relatives there.

And when she came back she boasted that she had passed for white and had seen "The Birth of a Nation" at the Princess Theater there.

"And it was a very good picture," she said. "I don't know what all the fuss over here was about."

Well, that was enough for me. If Mrs. Nixola Green liked the picture, then I was glad that Rat got the birth of a notion.

9

RAT JOINER WHIPS THE KAISER

Although it is still a subject of heated debate on Billy Goat Hill, Mayor Frank K. Haslett could not possibly have known what he was starting when he inaugurated the local campaign of the Liberty Stamp Contest for Colored in Hopkinsville, Ky. Mayor Haslett announced the contest at a special chapel assembly in the Booker T. Washington Colored Grammar School.

Our State was going to help Uncle Sam whip the Kaiser, he said, and our good colored citizens were going to be given an opportunity to participate. The Liberty Stamp Contest for Colored was being sponsored by the Governor himself in every town of more than 2,000 colored citizens—and the grand prize was staggering indeed. The little black boy or girl who sold the most Liberty Stamps in each town would be sent to the State Capitol to meet the Governor. And the face of the most representative winner would be placed on a placard for display in all of the colored grammar schools in the State.[1]

It was the first time that a mayor had visited the Booker T. Washington Colored Grammar School, and everybody was so excited that they hardly heard what he was saying. As things turned out, it might have been better for all concerned if nobody had heard the mayor. For then, Rat Joiner would not have whispered to me:

"I'm gonna win that thing just as sure as God is white. And I'd like to see somebody try to stop me."

I didn't pay Rat much mind at the time because I knew I was watching history in the making. Mr. Haslett was not only the first *mayor* to visit the Booker T. Washington Colored Grammar School; he was a *Democratic* mayor—and the first Democrat to hold that office in the history of the town. And Mayor Haslett had been elected through the Negro vote, although not a single colored citizen in Hopkinsville had cast a vote for him.

It happened like this. The Republicans had always controlled our town because our colored citizens outnumbered our white citizens two to one. And a large number of our colored Republicans branded as pure Democratic propaganda the tales that went around that Abraham Lincoln had been shot some fifty-two years before.

As the years went on, however, the Democrats kept getting stronger and stronger. Not that our colored citizens shifted their party affiliations; they just stopped taking the trouble to vote. Until finally, Judge Hezekiah Witherspoon, our town's Republican leader, got worried. He called his Republican City Council together.

"Look," he said (according to Mr. Jim Williams, our colored janitor in the Courthouse), "We've been missing a big bet. The Eighth of August is a big colored holiday. They celebrate 'Mancipation Proclamation or something then. Not one of 'em goes to work that day. Well, why don't we take advantage of it. If we will only shift Election Day from April 4 to August 8, there would be so many Republicans running around loose that the Democrats would think old Abe himself was on the ballot."

The City Council didn't even debate the question, Mr. Jim Williams said. They voted for the change right off.

It really was a very brilliant idea. But Judge Hezekiah Witherspoon either forgot or never knew one thing. The Younglove Street Baptist and the Dirt's Avenue Methodist Churches had been holding a joint picnic on Emancipation Day for forty-two years, and no mere election was liable to make much change in their plans.

It made an awful change in Judge Witherspoon's plans though. For when the new Election Day finally rolled around, there were 3,000 more colored citizens at Dan Massie's Picnic Grove than at all the polling places combined. So we woke up the next morning with our first Democratic mayor.

Judge Witherspoon was very much put out by the results, although the Republicans managed to elect a bare majority in the City Council. He ordered his majority to vote Election Day right back to April 4, and they did it again over Mayor Haslett's veto.

Judge Witherspoon was so mad that he stopped speaking to Miss Willie Sims, his colored cook, for three whole days. Except to warn her that it would serve us right if that Democratic so-and-so took the vote away from all the colored people—like the Republicans always said they would.

So that was why I wasn't listening to Rat Joiner when he whispered to me. For, not only had Mayor Frank K. Haslett made no move to take the vote away from the colored citizens, but here he was standing on the chapel platform of the Booker T. Washington Colored Grammar School and asking us to help the Governor whip the Kaiser.

I didn't think about Rat Joiner anymore until we were back at our double seat in the classroom. But while Miss Annabelle Breckenridge, our Fourth Grade teacher, was explaining that we had never lost a war (including the one between the States) I asked Rat if he was serious.

"You doggone tootin' I'm serious," he said. "And you better not tell anybody neither."

I had learned as early as the Second Grade—as had every other healthy youth under 135 pounds—to respect Rat's wishes, so I didn't tell anybody. But somehow or other the story got out. And it caused quite a laugh in certain quarters. Mrs. Nixola Green, our colored social leader, even made a joke about it.

"Wouldn't it be just awful if that Joiner brat did win the contest?" she asked. "Do you think they could print his picture without using white ink? And if his face was really put on a placard, the

National Advancement Society would probably sue the Governor for libel—for printing a caricature of the Negro race."

Now this would have been a very funny joke if *I* had made it. For I was only a half-shade lighter than Rat myself. In fact, he and I had busted a few collective noses when somebody started calling us the Gold Dust Twins. But it was very bad taste for anybody as light as Mrs. Nixola Green to refer to Rat's color. There were very strict social amenities on this question in Hopkinsville. It was especially bad for Mrs. Nixola Green since she was suspected of being the leader of the secret Blue Vein Society which dominated our social life in Hopkinsville. And nobody as dark as me and Rat had ever been invited to the parties she gave for her little niece, Sarah Williams.

All in all, Mrs. Nixola Green's little joke created quite a stir in our town. Especially up on Billy Goat Hill, where Rat lived, and where our colored citizens boasted a high degree of visibility. It was even rumored that the 100% colored citizens were planning to get in behind Rat and buy enough Liberty Stamps to make sure that he won. There was much grumbling about the yallers in general and Mrs. Nixola Green in particular. There was even talk of having her removed as Chairman of the Liberty Stamps Contest for Colored.

Except for a noticeable coolness on the part of Billy Goat Hill in meeting its quota, however, everything had apparently quieted down when the first week's results were announced at the Booker T. Washington Colored Grammar School. Little Aurelia Tandy, the niece of our leading undertaker, headed the list with $5.50 worth of Liberty Stamps. And Rat Joiner was nineteenth down the line— with only $1.75 to his credit. The second week was even worse. Fourteen contestants had sold more than $10.00 worth of stamps and Rat had a total of only $2.25.

By the morning that the Liberty Stamp Contest for Colored was scheduled to end, *l'affair Joiner* was definitely a dead and theoretical issue.

There was little doubt about the winner of the contest as we filed into our classrooms that morning. The names of the leaders were written on the blackboard in each room, and the race was due to close promptly at 10:30 A.M. The official winner would be announced at our eleven o'clock chapel assembly.

Little Aurelia Tandy—sandy-haired, blue eyes, and freckles—was still out front with $21.75. Sarah Williams, Mrs. Nixola Green's niece, was second with $14.50. And Rat was next to last from the bottom with only $3.75 to his credit. A few contestants turned in quarters and half dollars that morning, but these belated additions made no change in the standings.

We had just finished our history lesson at 10:15 (in which we learned how that old likker-head, Ulysses Simpson Grant, had overwhelmed pure and kindly Mr. Robert E. Lee) when Rat approached our Fourth Grade teacher, Miss Annabelle Breckenridge, and stood before her desk.

"In the name of the patriotic citizens of Billy Goat Hill," he said very carefully (as if he had been practicing it for at least three weeks), "I would like to buy me some Liberty Stamps to help our Guv'nor whip the Kaiser."

He then placed $31.50 on her desk.

Miss Breckenridge was so surprised, she stood there speechless. Finally she blurted: "You should've turned this money in earlier!"

Rat looked her straight in the eye. "The contest don't close until 10:30 A.M. this morning," he said. "I still got fourteen minutes."

Miss Annabelle Breckenridge flushed (She was almost as light as Mrs. Nixola Green) and her still startled gaze darted from Rat to the clock. Without another word she turned and left the room. She was gone so long that Tack-Haired Baker slipped out into the hall to get a drink of water. He came back and said that Miss Annabelle Breckenridge had gone in the office of our Principal, Professor P. Lowe, and that both of them were talking on the telephone.[2] Tack wasn't sure but he thought he heard one of them say "Nixola."

Miss Breckenridge came back about fifteen minutes later and picked up her geography book. She threw one quick glance in Rat's direction and plunged into our lesson. We were traveling rapidly through Asia when chapel time arrived, but Miss Breckenridge kept right on teaching. And strangely enough, the chapel assembly bell didn't ring. We swept through Turkey and got deep into Russia—but still no assembly bell. Finally, at 11:45, just when we were fixing to tackle Africa, the bell pealed out for chapel.

It turned out to be an historical chapel session in the Booker T. Washington Colored Grammar School, although it started out ordinarily enough. Professor P. Lowe, our principal, read some scripture. Miss H. Belle LaPrade gave a prayer.[3] And then Professor P. Lowe got up and introduced Mrs. Nixola Green, who was to announce the winner of the Liberty Stamp Contest for Colored.

The minute Mrs. Green started speaking I knew the story of Rat's *coup* had gotten around. For everybody started looking in our direction. Mrs. Nixola Green probably noticed it too, for she came right down to the point.

"I am sure that the Governor will appreciate our great contribution to his crusade to whip the Kaiser," she said, "especially the whole-hearted cooperation of our little boys and girls. It is really inspiring. Why, just this morning at 10:15 one of our industrious young men (with a nod in Rat's direction) actually turned in the amazing sum of $31.50. This raised his grand total to $35.25. I am sure that we all would like to congratulate this young man—Mr. Roosevelt Alonzo Taylor Joiner—"

Rat nudged me in the side and I started clapping, and the house came down in riotous applause. Rat looked modest for a moment and then he started to take a bow. He halted half way up, though, for Mrs. Nixola Green was still speaking:

"—and Mr. Joiner almost won the contest," she was saying, "*Almost* but not quite. For at 10:28 this morning—just two minutes before the deadline—little Miss Aurelia Tandy reported a $15. contribution from her beloved uncle and our esteemed mortician, Mr. Edward Smith. This raised her total to the grand sum of $36.75—"

Mrs. Green paused here for applause but none was forthcoming.

Abject and chaotic silence thundered through the room. And every eye was riveted on Rat Joiner. It was very awkward for a moment, but Rat Joiner rose to the occasion—and to his feet. Without a word, he picked up his books, his pencils and his ink bottle and headed for the back door of the chapel. The ear-racking silence still continued until Professor P. Lowe yelled out:

"Joiner! Sit down!"

Rat didn't even look back. He continued on up the center aisle.

Professor P. Lowe roared again, but with the same results. Miss Annabelle Breckenridge, who was sitting in the rear of the room, rushed to the back door and placed herself before it. Rat paused halfway up the aisle, regarded Miss Breckenridge soberly, and spoke for the first time. His voice was low-pitched and somber, but it echoed through the chapel:

"Git out from in front of that door."

Miss Breckenridge stood her ground firmly—and then ducked. Rat's ink bottle splattered against the door just above her head.

Its contents splashed into her hair and dripped down her astonished face and pink georgette waist. Professor P. Lowe was leaping from the rostrum—but too late. Rat Joiner was well out of the window.

Professor P. Lowe sprawled over a first row desk, but he was bellowing loudly as he went down:

"Get him! Get him! Get him!"

Our fallen Principal's voice galvanized the male population of the room into action. As a man, we leaped out of the three double windows and streaked through Garnett's Alley in hot pursuit of Rat Joiner.

A dozen of us overtook him ten blocks away. And all of us promptly went swimming.

Neither Professor P. Lowe, Miss Annabelle Breckenridge nor any of the contest directors were at the Booker T. Washington Colored Grammar School next morning. They had been summoned down to City Hall by Mayor Frank K. Haslett. It seems that a large delegation from Billy Goat Hill had been camping on the mayor's doorstep since sun-up, and he was investigating their highly vocal charge that "We wuz robbed!"

Professor P. Lowe and Mrs. Nixola Green heatedly denied the charges, but Mayor Haslett was undecided. He left both groups arguing with each other in his outer office while he went inside for consultation. He called Mr. Jim Williams, our courthouse janitor, into his private office and put it to him baldly.

"Jim," Mr. Jim Williams quoted him later as saying, "This is an awful mess to come up three days before election. I know all you people are mainly Republicans, but tell me this frankly, Jim: which group of you all got the most votes in Hopkinsville—the yallers or the blacks?"

Mr. Jim Williams said he scratched his head for a long, long time, and then he answered slowly:

"I really don't know, Mayor Haslett. I never thunk of it like that. It was always my idea that—to white people—all colored folks looked alike."

Mayor Haslett glared at Mr. Williams—but he decided to play it safe. He came out and announced that we could never defeat the Kaiser if we were a Nation divided. Therefore, in the name of American unity, Hopkinsville would send no representative to the Capitol with the other winners of the Liberty Stamp Contest for Colored.

Mrs. Nixola Green and the others didn't like it, but it proved to be a Solomon's choice. Billy Goat Hill went solidly Democratic for the first time in the next election, and Mr. Frank K. Haslett has been mayor ever since.

Of course they expelled Rat from the Booker T. Washington Colored Grammar School for the rest of the term. But he had the last laugh after all. The Governor finally picked the most representative winner of the Liberty Stamp Contest for Colored, and his picture was sent to the Booker T. Washington Colored Grammar School on a placard.

The winner, an energetic young man from Bowling Green, was three shades *darker* than Rat Joiner. And they didn't use any white ink to print his picture either.[4]

10

THE REVOLT OF
THE EVIL FAIRIES

The grand dramatic offering of the Booker T. Washington Colored Grammar School was the biggest event of the year in our social life in Hopkinsville, Kentucky. It was the one occasion on which they let us use the old Cooper Opera House, and even some of the white folks came out yearly to applaud our presentation. The first two rows of the orchestra were always reserved for our white friends, and our leading colored citizens sat right behind them— with an empty row intervening, of course.

Mr. Ed Smith, our local undertaker, invariably occupied a box to the left of the house and wore his cutaway coat and striped breeches. This distinctive garb was usually reserved for those rare occasions when he officiated at the funerals of our most prominent colored citizens. Mr. Thaddeus Long, our colored mailman, once rented a tuxedo and bought a box too. But nobody paid him much mind. We knew he was just showing off.

The title of our play never varied. It was always "Prince Charming and the Sleeping Beauty," but no two presentations were ever the same. Miss H. Belle LaPrade, our sixth-grade teacher, rewrote the script every season, and it was never like anything you read in the story books.

Miss LaPrade called it "a modern morality play of conflict between the forces of good and evil." And the forces of evil, of course, always came off second best.

The Booker T. Washington Colored Grammar School was in a state of ferment from Christmas until February, for this was the period when parts were assigned. First there was the selection of the Good Fairies and the Evil Fairies. This was very important, because the Good Fairies wore white costumes and the Evil Fairies black. And strangely enough most of the good Fairies usually turned out to be extremely light in complexion, with straight hair and white folks' features. On rare occasions a dark-skinned girl might be lucky enough to be a Good Fairy, but not one with a speaking part.

There never was any doubt about Prince Charming and the Sleeping Beauty. They were *always* light-skinned. And though nobody ever discussed those things openly, it was an accepted fact that a lack of pigmentation was a decided advantage in the Prince Charming and Sleeping Beauty sweepstakes.

And therein lay my personal tragedy. I made the best grades in my class, I was the leading debater, and the scion of a respected family in the community. But I could never be Prince Charming, because I was black.

In fact, every year when they started casting our grand dramatic offering my family started pricing black cheesecloth at Franklin's Department Store. For they knew that I would be leading the forces of darkness and skulking back in the shadows—waiting to be vanquished in the third act. Mamma had experience with this sort of thing. All my brothers had finished Booker T. before me.

Not that I was alone in my disappointment. Many of my classmates felt it too. I probably just took it more to heart. Rat Joiner, for instance, could rationalize the situation. Rat was not only black; he lived on Billy Goat Hill. But Rat summed it up like this:

"If you black, you black."

I should have been able to regard the matter calmly too. For our grand dramatic offering was only a reflection of our daily community life in Hopkinsville. The yallers had the best of everything. They held most of the teaching jobs in Booker T. Washington Colored Grammar School. They were the Negro doctors, the lawyers, the insurance men. They even had a "Blue Vein Society," and if your dark skin obscured your throbbing pulse you were hardly a member of the elite.

Yet I was inconsolable the first time they turned me down for Prince Charming. That was the year they picked Roger Jackson. Roger was not only dumb; he stuttered. But he was light enough to pass for white, and that was apparently sufficient.

In all fairness, however, it must be admitted that Roger had other qualifications. His father owned the only colored saloon in town and was quite a power in local politics. In fact, Mr. Clinton Jackson had a lot to say about just who taught in the Booker T. Washington Colored Grammar School. So it was understandable that Roger should have been picked for Prince Charming.

My real heartbreak, however, came the year they picked Sarah Williams for Sleeping Beauty. I had been in love with Sarah since kindergarten. She had soft light hair, bluish grey eyes, and a dimple which stayed in her left cheek whether she was smiling or not.

Of course Sarah never encouraged me much. She never answered any of my fervent love letters and Rat was very scornful of my one-sided love affair.[1] "As long as she don't call you a black baboon," he sneered, "you'll keep on hanging around."

After Sarah was chosen for Sleeping Beauty, I went out for the Prince Charming role with all my heart. If I had declaimed boldly in previous contests, I was matchless now. If I had bothered Mamma with rehearsals at home before, I pestered her to death this time. Yes, and I purloined my sister's can of Palmer's Skin Success.

I knew the Prince's role from start to finish, having played the head Evil Fairy opposite it for two seasons. And Prince Charming was one character whose lines Miss LaPrade never varied much in her many versions. But although I never admitted it, even to myself, I knew I was doomed from the start. They gave the part to Leonardius Wright. Leonardius, of course, was yaller.

The teachers sensed my resentment. They were almost apologetic. They pointed out that I had been such a splendid Head Evil Fairy for two seasons that it would be a crime to let anybody else try the role. They reminded me that Mamma wouldn't have to buy any more cheesecloth because I could use my same old costume. They insisted that the Head Evil Fairy was even more important than Prince Charming because he was the one who cast the spell on Sleeping Beauty. So what could I do but accept?

I had never liked Leonardius Wright. He was a goody-goody, and even Mamma was always throwing him up to me. But above all, he too was in love with Sarah Williams. And now he got a chance to kiss Sarah every day in rehearsing the awakening scene.

Well, the show must go on, even for little black boys. So I threw my soul into my part and made the Head Evil Fairy a character to be remembered. When I drew back from the couch of Sleeping Beauty and slunk away into the shadows at the approach of Prince Charming, my facial expression was indeed something to behold. When I was vanquished by the shining sword of Prince Charming in the last act, I was a little hammy perhaps—but terrific!

The attendance at our grand dramatic offering that year was the best in its history. Even the white folks overflowed the two rows reserved for them and a few were forced to sit in the intervening one. This created a delicate situation, but everybody tactfully ignored it.

When the curtain went up on the last act, the audience was in fine fettle. Everything had gone well for me too—except for one spot in the second act. That was where Leonardius unexpectedly' rapped me over the head with his sword as I slunk off into the shadows. That was not in the script, but Miss LaPrade quieted me down by saying it made a nice touch anyway. Rat said Leonardius did it on purpose.

The third act went on smoothly though until we came to the vanquishing scene. That was where I slunk from the shadows for the last time and challenged Prince Charming to mortal combat. The hero reached for his shining sword—a bit unsportsmanlike I

95

always thought, since Miss LaPrade consistently left the Head Evil Fairy unarmed—and then it happened!

Later, I protested loudly—but in vain—that it was a case of self-defense. I pointed out that Leonardius had a mean look in his eye. I cited the impromptu rapping he had given my head in the second act. But nobody would listen. They just wouldn't believe that Leonardius really intended to brain me when he reached for his sword.

Anyway he didn't succeed. For the minute I saw that evil gleam in his eye—or was it my own?—I cut loose with a right to the chin, and Prince Charming dropped his shining sword and staggered back. His astonishment lasted only a minute though, for he lowered his head and came charging in, fists flailing. There was nothing yellow about Leonardius but his skin.

The audience thought the scrap was something new Miss LaPrade had written in. They might have kept on thinking so if Miss LaPrade hadn't been screaming so hysterically from the sidelines. And if Rat Joiner hadn't decided that this was as good a time as any to settle old scores. So he turned around and took a sock at the male Good Fairy nearest him.

When the curtain rang down, the forces of Good and Evil were locked in combat. And Sleeping Beauty was wide awake, and streaking for the wings.

They rang the curtain back up fifteen minutes later, and we finished the play. I lay down and expired according to specifications, but Prince Charming will probably remember my sneering corpse to his dying day. They wouldn't let me appear in the grand dramatic offering at all the next year. But I didn't care. I couldn't have been Prince Charming anyway.

NOTES

1. MR. JACK JOHNSON AND ME

1. There is no official record that Robert Poston ever attended Princeton. According to the manager of Alumni Records and Mailing at Princeton, "Any person who even matriculates for one semester is carried in our files as an alumnus forever; so it seems unlikely Robert Poston ever attended Princeton."

However, a note in *The Marcus Garvey and Universal Negro Improvement Association Papers* says that Robert "briefly attended Princeton University during Woodrow Wilson's term as university president, but was forced to leave after protesting Wilson's policy of racial segregation on campus" (Berkeley: University of California Press, 1984) 3:694.

2. Robert L. Poston wrote an editorial for *The Negro World* in which he spoke seriously on the topic of Jack Johnson, "race amalgamation," and the importance of blacks maintaining a high standard of conduct, the theme that Ted Poston, in "Mr. Jack Johnson and Me," treats humorously. Robert L. Poston, "Jack Johnson—An Object Lesson," *The Negro World,* 18 Oct. 1921, 4.

3. *Skeeting* refers to pushing the water with the palm of the hand while swimming; it also means skimming rocks across the water (AW).

"Ted could swim like a fish. I never could keep up with him. We were baptized together at Virginia Street Church. We used to practice for it in the Little River which floods every spring. A bunch of us would baptize each other and see how long we could stay under the water. That was so we wouldn't be scared when the time came" (MQ).

2. THE WEREWOLF OF WOOLWORTH'S

1. "Lovier's Hill was straight out Hayes Street. They had four iron pipes coming out of the spring through a concrete structure. Everybody used to get water out of there—good water, too" (AW). "Lovier's Hill had a house that sat way back. On the east side there was a lane that was thickly wooded. You'd come to a spring and that was the most delicious water. It came out of the ground year round. They said that if anyone drank that water he would come back to Hopkinsville" (MDW).

2. "There was a friendly grocer named Wes Garnett who sold vegetables out of a wagon. He had a store at the corner of Second and Vine for a long time, with a little deli. He would cook chitterlings and ham. I remember one day Mama gave me a pan and sent me over there to get some chitterlings and I dropped the pan on the floor. I picked the chitterlings up and put them back in the pan and carried them home and Mama said, 'Jennie, what are all these little specks on these chitterlings?' and I said, 'Black pepper, I guess, Mama.' She saw through that and said, 'I believe you dropped these,' and I said, 'Yes, I did.' And I didn't get a whipping for that. I was so afraid I was going to get a spanking for telling a story— not so much for dropping the chitterlings but for telling a story. I got off that time and she was very nice about it. So, I guess—I don't know if she sent back for some more or what, but those came from Mr. Garnett's grocery" (JKB).

3. "A lot of farmers around here grew melons in little patches on the edge of town. Old Man Anthony used to pitch rock salt at you when you went in" (AW).

3. KNEE BABY WATKINS

1. In some cities, blacks could attend the theaters on specified days. In "Knee Baby Watkins," Poston may have invented the analogy that Negroes being considered acceptable theater patrons on Wednesdays and Saturdays, or only in the balcony, or on the same floor as whites as long as one row sat empty between them, was as arbitrary and ridiculous as a child deciding to walk only on two days a week.

Knee Baby Watkins may be modeled on "naughty" Frederick Douglass Poston, who shaped up only after he went to Male and Female College.

2. "There could have been an alley by Old Man Garnett's grocery on

Second and Vine. There were alleys in most blocks, for the sanitation wagon to get through to clean out the privies" (AW).

3. Jennie Knight Baker says that Miss Cecelia Coole's name was taken from Miss Jennie Poole, and Mrs. Rosa Coldweather's from Mrs. Rosa Morgan Merriweather: "These teachers were marvelous people. Mrs. Merriweather was an outstanding disciplinarian but not quite as good a teacher as Miss Poole. Mrs. Merriweather taught history. She put dates on the board and you had to memorize them."

"Mrs. Merriweather was always having someone bring a buckberry switch and she'd tan your hide. Then when you got home, you got another whipping. Everyone in town took responsibility for correcting you—'I'm gonna tell your *Mama*'" (AW).

Neither Miss Poole nor Mrs. Merriweather fits the picture Poston draws of his fictional teachers as petty, gossipy, and back-biting. Allison Williams adds, "I can't think of any teacher who knew Mrs. Mamie Bassett [wife of the mayor, Dr. Frank H. Bassett, Sr.] that well, either, unless she worked for her, because Mrs. Bassett would have no occasion to come in contact with the Negro teachers. I think this is something Ted made up in his own mind. There was no connection between most white and black people a'tall."

4. COUSIN BLIND MARY

1. "Cousin Blind Mary was a fortune-teller and people relied on her. My mother carried me to her once because Mama kinda believed in that. Blind Mary *could* tell fortunes. I asked Blind Mary if I would be getting married. She said, 'Yes, you'll get married.' I asked her, 'Well, how will it be?' and she said, 'You'll get a divorce.' I said, 'Will I marry again?' She said, 'Yes.' I said, 'Well, how will *that* one be?' She said, 'I don't see it.' But I didn't think about her predictions for years afterwards. Sure enough, what she told me came true. I never knew she was Ted's cousin. He may have made that up" (JKB).

2. "At one time taking measurements for suits got to be a racket around here. They had ads in all the Sunday School papers from over in Nashville which was the head place" (AW).

5. PAPA WAS A DEMOCRAT

1. "Mr. Poston was an outstanding Democrat. At that time there wasn't any Democrats here and a lot of people made fun of Mr. Poston. He had his trials," Rozelle Leavell comments.

2. Durrett's "Dirt's" Avenue was another black neighborhood that was gerrymandered out of the city limits for many years. Residents kept hogs, so the area smelled bad (AW).

Raymond Burse, who would graduate from Harvard Law School and become a Rhodes Scholar and eventually president of Kentucky State University fifty years after Eph Poston taught there, grew up on Durrett's Avenue.

3. Copper-Mouth Papa was Jim Lewis, not Oscar Peterson, Allison Williams says. "And Ted would not have knocked his teeth out. You didn't do that kind of thing to Jim Lewis. He was big, and—I'd *talk* to him, that's all. Anyway, Jim Lewis had bad teeth. He got a job as a bellhop at the Latham and when he was making pretty good money, he had all his teeth gold-plated, crowned, and got them one at a time so they were all different colors, different types of gold. We nicknamed him 'Copper-Mouth Papa.'"

4. "Miss Hazel Green sounds like Mrs. LaPrade. She could have said that colored people should not vote for Democrats. She was prejudiced in that she wanted to keep on the good side of white people. She had a lot of white friends" (JKB).

5. "That's comical as hell, that Ted could just think up something like his father carrying a gun. I can't imagine Ole Man Poston having a pistol in his hand" (AW).

6. MR. BEEFER JONES

1. The real name of Mr. Orlando "Beefer" Jones was Chester Haynes. "He ran a gambling joint called 'The Hundred.' Maybe that was its street number. It was at Ninth and the railroad. People would say, 'Let's go up to the Hundred'" (AW).

2. "Pete Postell probably sold that place to Chester Haynes. I knew about it when I was a child because Ches rented a little house from my parents on Fourth Street. He paid his rent—two dollars a week—on Monday morning, all in dimes, after gambling the whole weekend" (JKB).

3. "I do believe those were the Brooks brothers, nephews, not cousins.

One was chocolate brown, always laughing and joking. James would sneak around to get revenge. Chester Haynes indulged the boys too much" (JKB).

4. The anecdote about Mr. Beefer Jones's mother rubbing a piece of fat on his lips before he went to school so that no one would realize he had had no breakfast is one of the most poignant in Ted Poston's repertoire, but Poston manages to make even this humorous with an upbeat ending.

5. A *fader* is one who starts the action in a card game and then drops out, as a claquer at the opera starts the applause (AW).

6. In a crap game, *set the meat* means to throw the money out on the table because a win is at hand (AW).

7. HIGH ON THE HOG

1. "Bake was about my complexion [light] but he had the tightest-knotted hair. It was James Mimms who called him 'Tack-Haired Baker' first" (AW).

The Mumford family on Cottage Street probably provided the model for Mr. Fertilizer Ferguson, Allison Williams figures: "There were a whole slew of Mumfords. They were wealthy, with oil wells in Oklahoma. They sold twenty or thirty houses that they had bought or built. Robert Mumford made a fortune cleaning outhouses. He was the forerunner of the sanitation department. One son is a Holiness preacher now, at the Sanctified Church, and drives a Cadillac. He is well respected.

"The Mumfords were no known kin to Tack-Haired Baker. 'Bake' had no kin except his mother, unless it was the tailor, Ned Turner. His mother was so playful. Mrs. Fanny Baker was a hard-working, fun-loving woman who doted on her son. She was the cook at Bethel College. Everyone said Ned Turner was Bake's father. She would joke along about it and say yes. Reuben hated to be teased about that. His mother was just as good-hearted as she could be. I don't think she ever had three hundred dollars cash in her life, but she *gave* him everything a person could want, although I think Ned Turner gave him most of it. I'm sure Ted helped Bake as much as he could. As the expression goes, Reuben wasn't 'well-wrapped.' But he got with the bunch, and we just took care of him" (AW).

2. Uncle John Braxton was an early rapper. "If you asked him a question, he would answer in rhyme" (JKB).

"One of the major cultural differences between the white middle class and . . . Afro-Americans is that the latter have preserved an oral-aural world view while the former have invested their creative energies and imaginations heavily in books. . . . Many ethnocentric judgments about blacks stem from the white man's inability to understand or appreciate the creative aspects of living in an oral atmosphere. . . . A good talker as judged by ghetto Negroes is often regarded by whites as hostile and arrogant. . . . Verbal contest accounts for a large portion of talk. Proverbs, turns of phrase, jokes are used not for purposes of discursive communication but as weapons in verbal battle. Any gathering of men may turn into a teasing or boasting session. . . . Preaching demands the same type of word control. . . . Creativity is a device for social approval." Roger D. Abrahams, *Deep Down in the Jungle: Negro Narrative Folklore from the Streets of Philadelphia* (New York: Aldine, 1970), 39, 43, 59, 13.

3. Poston chides ostentation and pretension in whites as much as he does in Blue Vein Society members in the black community. Blacks much resented that whites would go to any extreme to call them by their first names and yet would address their fellow whites as "Mr." and "Mrs."

4. The Dixie Cafe, on the north side of Ninth Street between Main and Virginia, was owned by Gus the Greek. "Ted and I sold him bullfrogs. They cost five dollars a pound now—six legs to a pound. They're a delicacy. You skin them, soak them in milk, flour them, and fry them. They're so pretty and white. They look like fish meat. When we were kids we went down in the creek of the Little River and we'd get twenty-five and thirty big bullfrogs, a gunny-sack half-full, and sell them for twenty-five cents a pair of legs" (AW).

5. Fertilizer Ferguson recalls the way colored bellhops and waiters adapted to their calling for the sake of bigger tips. "A white fellow went in the hotel and walked up to the head waiter. He said, 'Say, boy, are you the head nigger here?' 'No, I'm the head, but I'm not the head nigger. We're colored gentlemen who work in this hotel.' The guy would say, 'Oh, I was lookin' for the head nigger. I'm Mr. So and So from So and So down South. When I leave, I generally give the head nigger a hundred dollars.' 'Oh! You lookin' for the *head* nigger! Hell, boss! *You* knows I'se the head nigger *here!*'" (AW).

8. THE BIRTH OF A NOTION

1. "The Birth of a Notion" was published in Herbert Hill's anthology *Soon, One Morning* as "Rat Joiner Routs the Klan." When Ted Poston was nine years old, in 1915, the three-hour silent film *Birth of a Nation* by D. W. Griffith was released. Griffith, born on a Kentucky farm in 1875, depicted the Civil War and its aftermath in the South. The film caused riots in some cities due to its racism and its approving look at the rise of the Ku Klux Klan. It showed black men as aggressive, in pursuit of white women.

2. Jelly Roll Benson is modeled on "Jello" Danforth who "wasn't but three feet and a half tall. He couldn't find any long pants; they were all too long for him," Allison Williams says. "I used to tell a story on Jello about him and Dr. Bassett. Jello got so mad when I'd tell this.

"Dr. Bassett had built up quite a following in Hopkinsville. There was a saying among the politicians that you couldn't beat Dr. Bassett for nothing. To show an example, there was a raiding of a crap game and Dr. Bassett heard about it. He went down to the police station. They had all the guys who were participating in the crap game locked up and he saw that one of the fellows was this friend of his, Jello Danforth. So Dr. Bassett said, 'Jello, what are *you* doing in here?' One of the police said, 'Oh, he was gambling.' Dr. Bassett said, 'Why, he ain't got sense enough to gamble. Don't you know he don't know nothin' about gambling?' Says, 'Say, boy.' 'Yassuh, Dr. Bassett.' 'Who's the President of the United States?' 'Dr. Bassett, you know you's the President of the United States.'

"That shows what kind of a following Dr. Bassett had. Jello would get fighting mad when I'd tell that on him. Jello was trying to get out of jail and Dr. Bassett was helping him find a way. Jello was playing dumb."

3. Since Lucy means light and clarity, Poston may be naming her with tongue in cheek. She scarcely perceives the people with whom she interacts weekly.

9. RAT JOINER WHIPS THE KAISER

1. The "most representative" Negro being sought to win the Liberty Bond Contest, Poston intimates, would be the "most white."

2. "Pleasant Moore [P. Long or P. Lowe in the fiction] was tall, of large stature and dark. We called him 'Foots Moore' because he had long feet

and fingers and he'd point those fingers at you. He'd slap this finger up beside his nose—like this—it was just so amusing" (JKB).

3. "Mrs. H. Belle LaPrade was a little short lady who wore a wig. She was the forerunner of the beauty parlor. When she got out of school, you'd see her with her little black bag and she took care of all the rich women's hair up Main Street" (AW).

"Mrs. LaPrade, not Miss Hazel Green, was the third grade teacher. She had exquisite handwriting. I try to write like she did" (MDW).

"We had Mrs. LaPrade in third, fifth, and sixth grades. She was moved around a lot. Her husband, Professor LaPrade, taught out in the country. He had such a big 'dick' he had to keep it strapped to his leg, kids said. Kids used to talk about things like that. Mrs. LaPrade sure was a good teacher, though. She taught me 'Blessings on thee little man, barefoot boy with cheeks of tan.' She made me say that nine thousand times until I got it right" (AW).

"When we were boys, we were scared of the professor. That old Mrs. Belle LaPrade, you come with a baseball bat, she'd get her one. 'I done told you now!' Yessir, they was tough. We gloried in 'em" (TRJ).

4. Ironically, in "Rat Joiner Whips the Kaiser," Rat Joiner is really whipping the enemies close to home, the "high yallers." He is helping the governor to combat the intraracial bigotry exemplified by the Blue Vein Society.

10. THE REVOLT OF THE EVIL FAIRIES

1. Mary Duncan Wilson, the model for little Sarah Williams, denies that she spurned Ted Poston: "Ted was my best boyfriend. I don't think in my young life there was ever anybody like Ted. He was brilliant and I admired his intelligence. And I liked his family. It was as much puppy love as you'll ever find. I don't think Ted was justified [in suggesting that his love was unrequited]. I was bashful. There were other boys who liked me and I gave them the cold shoulder, too. My father was always telling me, 'Wait a while.' I was overly protected and had a lot of restrictions. Maybe the things that *Ted* thought meant I was turning him away were just family restrictions."

SOURCES

PRIMARY

Bacon, Clara. Hopkinsville, Ky. Personal interview, 7 Feb. 1984.

Baker, Jennie Knight. Hopkinsville. Personal interviews, 7, 8, 9, 10, 19, 21 Jan. 1984; 12, 18 Jan. 1985.

Banks, Ruth. Tucson, Ariz., and New York City. Personal interviews, 22 Aug. 1983; 29 June 1984. Letters to author, 13 Sept., 17 Oct., 7 Dec. 1983; 2 Jan., 3, 21 Feb., 15 Mar., 16 Apr., 18 May, 5, 21 Aug., 15 Sept. 1984; 23, 31 Jan., 20 Feb., 2 Apr. 1985.

Bronaugh, Charles W. Hopkinsville. Personal interview, 13 Feb. 1984.

Brown, Jasper. Hopkinsville. Personal interview, 3 July 1983.

Burse, Raymond M. Frankfort, Ky. Letter to author, 17 June 1983. Personal interview, 13 Oct. 1983.

Clark, Rebecca Quarles. Hopkinsville. Personal interviews, 10 Oct. 1983; 24 Mar. 1984. [Died 10 Jan. 1985]

Conover, Mrs. Jerry H. Letters to author, 9 Nov. 1982; 11 Oct. 1983.

Eckman, Fern Marja. New York City and New Milford, Conn. Letters to author, 24 Sept., 31 Oct., 8 Nov. 1984; 16 June 1985. Personal interview, 13 Oct. 1984.

Johnston, Ernie, Jr. New York City. Personal interview, 29 June 1984. Letters to the author, 25 July 1984; 12 Jan. 1985.

Joiner, Philip. Hopkinsville. Personal interviews, 12 Mar. 1984; 2 Feb. 1985.

Joiner, Theodore Roosevelt "Rat." Hopkinsville. Personal interview, 8 Oct. 1983. [Died 11 Dec. 1984]

Knight, Frances Wagner. Hopkinsville. Personal interviews, 15, 18, 28 Feb. 1984. [Died Nov. 1984]

Leavell, Rosa. Hopkinsville. Personal interview, 3 July 1983. [Deceased]

Leavell, Rozelle. Hopkinsville. Personal interview, 3 July 1983. [Deceased]

Lewis, Diana Bonnor. New York City. Letters to author, 9, 19 Sept., 29 Nov., 5 Dec. 1983; 21, 30 Jan., 2, 4 Feb. 1984; 4 Mar. 1985. Telephone interview, 29 Nov. 1983. Personal interview, 29 Dec. 1984. [Died 1987]

Lynch, J. T. Hopkinsville. Letter to author, 24 Mar. 1984.

Major, Brooks. Hopkinsville. Personal interview, 12 Feb. 1984. Letters to author, 30 Oct., 27 Nov. 1984.

Moon, Henry Lee. Long Island City, New York. Personal interviews, 15 July, 4 Aug., 16, 30 Sept. 1982; 27 May, 14 Aug., 28 Sept., 28 Nov. 1983; 29 June 1984. Letter to author, 11 Jan. 1984. [Died 1985]

Moten, Lydia Braxton. Hopkinsville. Personal interview, 3 July 1983. [Deceased]

Palmer, Johnella Braxton. Hopkinsville. Personal interview, 3 July 1983. [Deceased]

Poston, Ersa Hines. McLean, Va. Letters to author, 21 Apr., 4 May, 26 Aug. 1982; 27 June, 30 Aug., 1 Dec. 1983; 1 Mar., 19 Nov. 1984; 28 May 1985. Personal interview, 5 July 1983.

Quarles, Marcus. Hopkinsville. Telephone interview, 9 July 1983. [Deceased]

Torian, Bernice Bell. Hopkinsville. Telephone interview, 1 Feb. 1985.

Turner, William T. Hopkinsville. Personal interviews, 15, 19, 22 Mar. 1984.

Wagner, Willie Mabry. Hopkinsville. Letter to author, 7 Dec. 1984.

Williams, Allison. Hopkinsville. Letters to author, telephone and personal interviews, 3 July 1983 to 11 Feb. 1985. [Died 1989]

Wilson, Mary Duncan. Indianapolis. Letters to author, 28 Sept., 14, 24 Oct., 15 Dec. 1983; 12 Jan., 15 Feb., 30 Apr. 1985. Telephone interview, 28 Sept. 1983. Personal interviews, 9 Oct. 1983; 10, 11 Feb. 1985.

Wooldridge, Roberta Mabry. Hopkinsville. Personal interview, 21 Apr. 1984. Telephone interview, 15 Dec. 1984. [Deceased]

SECONDARY

Books

Abrahams, Roger D. *Deep Down in the Jungle: Negro Narrative Folklore from the Streets of Philadelphia.* New York: Aldine, 1970.

Caron's City Directory for Hopkinsville, 1907.

Catalogue, Kentucky State Normal and Industrial Institute, 1913–1914. Frankfort, Ky.

Sources

Major, Clarence. *Dictionary of Afro-American Slang*. New York: International, 1970.

Turner, William T. *Gateway to the Past*. Vol. 2. Hopkinsville, Ky.: Pennyroyal Museum, 1981.

Walden College Catalog, 1921–1922. Nashville, Tenn.

Newspapers and Periodicals

Eckman, Fern Marja. "Ted Poston—Newspaperman." *New York Post*, 14 Apr. 1972, 55.

"Forrest-Poston." Hopkinsville, Ky., *The New Age*. 25 Apr. 1924, 1.

"Hon. Marcus Garvey Assures the People." *The Negro World*, 1 Apr. 1922, 9.

"A Liberty Bond in Every Home" (advertisement). *The Hopkinsville Kentuckian*, 6 June 1917, 8.

"Mr. Robert L. Poston." *The Negro World*, 6 Oct. 1923, 5.

"Peter Postell, 72, Dies at Home Here." *Kentucky New Era*, 8 Apr. 1944, 3.

[Postell, Fannie B.] "News of Interest to Negro Citizens: Funerals Conducted." *Kentucky New Era*, 17 Nov. 1953, 2.

"Robert Poston Dies on Ship." *Kentucky New Era*, 31 Mar. 1924, 4.

Webber, Harry B. "Radiogram Tells of End on 'Roosevelt': Returning from Liberian Mission; Recently Married Famous Sculptress; Well Known in Detroit." *Pittsburgh Courier*, 22 Mar. 1924, 1.

Official Documents

Christian County Census. 1900. Sheet B, no. 8, Ward 5.

Christian County Colored School Census. 1895, 1896, 1910, 1911, 1914, 1915, 1916.

Christian Co. Marriage Bonds and Licenses. Book 10, pp. 64–65. Ephraim Poston and Mollie Cox, 22 Dec. 1887.

Christian County *Register of Deeds*. Book 108, pp. 1–2. Jno. A. and Annie Gunn conveyed to E. Poston and Mollie Poston, property on south side of Hayes Street, 1 Jan. 1902.

Kentucky Vital Statistics Records. Death certificates for Mollie Poston, 31 May 1917; Roberta Poston, 15 Apr. 1919; and Lillian Poston, 10 Oct. 1927.